YES MATRON

WHITE ROW

Peggy Donaldson

To all 'Royal' nurses, past, present and future

YES MATRON

WHITE ROW

Peggy Donaldson

First published 1989 by
the White Row Press Ltd
135 Cumberland Road, Dundonald
Belfast BT16 0BB

Reprinted 1989

The publisher gratefully acknowledges the assistance of the Advisory Committee on Trust Funds of the Royal Victoria Hospital, Belfast, in the publication of this book.

Front cover: Miss Lydia Newman, Lady Superintendent 1886–1928; the first batch of newly qualified 'Royal' nurses to become redundant, as photographed by the *Belfast Telegraph*, November 1984. Back cover: (pbk): Nightingale ward, 1923. Front flap: Nurse in cloak, 1938. Back Flap: First year badge.

Illustrated with line drawings by Joan O'Neill

British Library Cataloguing in Publication Data
Donaldson, Peggy
    Yes matron: a history of nurses and nursing at the Royal Victoria Hospital Belfast, 1797 – 1988.
    1.   Great Britain. Medicine. Nursing, to 1988
    I.   Title
    610.73'0941

ISBN 1 870132 15 7 Paperback
ISBN 1 870132 20 3 Hardback

Typeset by December Publications, Belfast
Printed by the Universities Press Ltd, Belfast

Contents

Acknowledgements

Without the help of a great many past and present members of the nursing staff of the Royal Victoria Hospital, Belfast this book could not have been written. Particular thanks are due to Miss M.K.Robb, Matron of the Hospital from 1966 to 1973, for first suggesting that there was a need for a history of nursing in the hospital, and for much additional help; to Miss F.E.Elliott Matron of the hospital from 1946 to 1966 for a vast amount of material and for encouragement, comment and criticism; to Miss F.K.Betty, Miss M.A.McFarland and Mrs R.Simpson for material and for verifying completed chapters; to Mr H.A.Reid for much useful data and particularly for his help in providing many of the photographs. Thanks also to all those who took time and trouble to write and send invaluable data, many of them from overseas, and to those who spared time to provide equally invaluable oral evidence – and often tea as well! Among the contributors were: Mrs C.C. Amobi, Mrs J. Arnold, Miss H.M.C. Barratt, Mrs H. Black, Miss B. Boyce, Mrs Pat Brown, Miss M. Burch, Miss G. Creighton, Mrs A.B. Cross, Mrs M. Crothers, Mrs O. Daly, Miss R.G. Dawson, Mrs G.I. Deas, Mrs J. Elliott, Mrs G. Fenton, Mr Frank Finn, Mrs W.E. Flewett, Mrs V. Fullerton, Miss M.A. Galbraith, Miss H. Gaw, Mrs T.C. Geary, the late Mrs M. Gilliland, Miss A. Grant, Mrs M. Gray, Miss N. Grindle, Mrs H. Hanna, Mrs H.A. Hezlett, Mrs E. Lacey, Mrs J. Law, the late Miss E. Mitchell, Mrs J. Mercer, the late Miss A. Montague, the late Miss A.J. McAdam, Mrs F. McLardy, Mrs A.E. McCombe, Miss D. McCullough, Mrs A. McDonald, Mrs I. McDonagh, Mrs E. Mullen, Mrs T. Pearn, Miss A. Porter,Mrs A.P.I. Ritchie, Mrs S. Ritchie, Mrs J. Ryder, Mrs J.J. Robb, Mrs R. Shannon, Mrs E. Smiley, Mrs P. Stalker, Mrs B. Swain, Mrs J.W. Taggart, Mrs J.W. Taylor, Mrs T. Young. For those whose names have been inadvertently omitted from this list, my apologies, and to those who wished to remain anonymous my thanks as well. I am also grateful for the help given by the late Dr H.G. Calwell, former Honorary Archivist of the RVH; Dr J.S. Logan the present Honorary Archivist and by his wife, the latter an invaluable source of information for the war years; Mrs Olive Russell, secretary to the Archivist; Mr M.E. Bradley, Director of Nurse Education in the Belfast Northern College of Nursing; Sir Ian Fraser, Professor O.L. Wade and Professor Sir Graham Bull, former members of the Consultant Medical Staff of the Hospital; Dr Margaret Campbell; Dr Monica Baly, who was an invaluable source of advice regarding the Nightingale papers; Mr C.E.B. Brett; Miss Joyce Long for critical comment; Miss Agnes McMaster; Miss Judy Nelson; and Dr R.W.M. Strain.

Last but by no means least, thanks are due to my husband, who not only encouraged the project and was an invaluable factual and literary critic, casting an expert eye over each chapter as it was produced, but who put up with a great deal of neglect in the process.

Preface

In April 1797, a small six-bed fever hospital was opened in Belfast in a house in Factory Row (now Berry Street) in association with the existing voluntary dispensary. Doctors gave their services free to both dispensary and hospital, but for the latter one paid nurse was employed to care for the patients. No record remains to show who she was, where she came from, what her qualifications were or how much she was paid. She remains totally anonymous and yet has an important place in history, for she was the first of the long line of nurses who have cared, and still are caring, for the sick in the hospital now known as the Royal Victoria, Belfast. What follows is their story, and to a lesser extent the story of the hospital itself.

The history of the Royal Victoria Hospital, from its dispensary origins in 1792 to 1953, has been written by three eminent members of the Visiting Medical Staff, Doctors Malcolm, Allison and Marshall. Understandably, as medical men their emphasis is on that particular aspect of the work. To an ex-nurse of the hospital, however, the coverage given to nurses and nursing is woefully inadequate – but no more so than in histories written of many other hospitals.

This book is an attempt to restore the balance, and as such refers relatively seldom to the work of the doctors or administrators, except where they relate to the nursing work of the hospital. As an essential background however, an outline of the development of the hospital within the period concerned is included in each chapter.

To avoid repetition, some aspects of life in the hospital have been dealt with almost exclusively within a specific period but, as those who have worked there will know, certain practices and experiences have been shared by more than one generation. Thus, most of the story of the wardsmaids is contained in Chapter Three, while, for example, Christmas in the hospital is largely covered in the following chapter.

Glossary

Angiocardiography – A specialised type of X-ray of the heart and blood vessels

Appendicectomy – removal of the appendix

Aseptic – sterile, cleared of all infection

Block study – a system introduced into nurse training whereby nurses were removed from the wards for periods (blocks) of days, weeks or months to study in the school. The purpose was to separate lectures and study from ward work.

Cardiology/ist – heart disease/specialist

Consultants – popular, but slightly inaccurate, name for members of the Visiting Medical Staff. It more properly should refer to former members of the VMS who were appointed to the Honorary Consultant Medical Staff.

Day surgery – when patients are brought in for minor surgery and go home the same day

Dermatology/ist – skin diseases/specialist

Electrocardiography (ECG) – electrical recording of the heart's action

Fractured femur – broken thigh bone

Gastro-enterology – diseases of the stomach and bowel

Gynaecology (gynae)/ist – women's diseases/specialist

Haematology – blood diseases

Houseman – a resident house physician or surgeon. In the nineteenth century the RHS also acted as Superintendent. This was later a separate appointment and housemen were newly-qualified doctors who worked in the hospital for six or twelve months only.

Metabolic – diseases of the ductless glands, the commonest being diabetes and disorders of the thyroid gland

Nephritis – inflammation of the kidney

Neurology – diseases of the nervous system not usually treated by surgery

Neurosurgery – surgery of the brain and nervous system

Omnopon and Scopolamine – a pre-anaesthetic medication

Ophthalmology (Ophthalmics) – eye diseases

Orthopaedics – bone disorders (a specialty often linked with the treatment of broken bones)

Perforated – burst

Pupils – resident medical students

Pyelitis – inflammation of the lining of the kidney

Radiography/er – X-ray/non-medical person who takes X-rays

Rheumatology – rheumatic and allied diseases

Stomatherapist – specialist in dealing with patients needing or having artificial openings (stoma) in different parts of the body – usually the bowel

Take-in (on) – the term used in the Royal for a ward taking its turn to admit emergencies.

Thrombo-phlebitis – an inflamed blood vessel with a clot in it

Trephining – drilling holes in the skull to relieve pressure

Vascular surgery – surgery of the blood vessels

Venereology – venereal diseases

Visiting Medical Staff or Medical Staff – senior doctors appointed to serve on the hospital staff. Before 1948 these were honorary appointments. The Medical Staff met as a body to discuss medical matters. When the numbers became too large the Medical Staff Committee was elected.

Abbreviations

ADNS – Assistant Director of Nursing Services
ARRC – Associate of the Royal Red Cross
DANO – District Administrative Nursing Officer
DNO – Divisional Nursing Officer
DNS – Director of Nursing Services
EHSSB – Eastern Health and Social Services Board
Health Board, – Area Health and Social Services Board
Joint Council – Joint Nursing and Midwives Council for Northern Ireland
KEB – King Edward VII Memorial Building
N.I.Council – Northern Ireland Council for Nurses, Midwives and Health Visitors.
N.I.Board – Northern Ireland Board of the UKCC
NO – Nursing Officer
PNO – Principal Nursing Officer
RBHSC – Royal Belfast Hospital for Sick Children
RCN – Royal College of Nursing
RMH – Royal Maternity Hospital
RVH – Royal Victoria Hospital
SNA – Student Nurses Association
SNO – Senior Nursing Officer
UKCC – United Kingdom Central Council for the Training of Nurses, Midwives and
    Health Visitors.

Illustrations

Every effort has been made to attribute the photographs used here, but it has not
always been possible to find the source of prints held by individuals for many years.
My apologies for any errors or omissions.

1 The Early Years 1797 – 1870

Belfast's situation at the mouth of the river Lagan and within the sheltering arms of Belfast Lough has long made it an ideal trading centre, both for the produce of the country and for goods brought from overseas. By the 1790s the foundations had already been laid for the phenomenal growth that was to take place in the town's trade, industry and population. There was, however, one major disadvantage in being a popular meeting place. Travellers arriving by land or sea all too often brought with them contagious or infectious fevers which, helped by the overcrowded and unhealthy living conditions of the poor of the town, soon reached epidemic proportions. With monotonous regularity typhus, relapsing fever, dysentery, typhoid and small pox ravaged the town.[1] The black cloud of cholera loomed some distance ahead. Consumption (tuberculosis) reaped a regular harvest.

It was known that the isolation of fever victims, particularly if they could be housed in better conditions than were commonly found in the homes of the poor, not only gave them a better chance of recovery but also helped prevent the spread of infection. Before 1797, the only refuge for the sick poor of Belfast – the more well-to-do remained at home when ill – was in the small infirmary of the Charitable Society's poorhouse. These beds, however, were reserved for the inmates of the poorhouse. For the others, there was nothing.

In 1792 a group of local doctors, clergy, business and professional men, concerned about the lack of medical aid for the poor of the town, raised funds to open a voluntary dispensary. Patients were treated without charge either at the dispensary or in their own homes. The doctors who visited the patients at home were particularly frus-

Belfast from Cromac Wood c.1793, by John Nixon. This idyllic view belies the fact that Belfast was unsanitary, overcrowded and unhealthy, and its port as much a source of disease as wealth. (Ulster Museum, Belfast)

trated as they saw fevers spread like wildfire because the first victims could not be isolated. This frustration eventually led to the decision to open a small fever hospital in association with the dispensary. In 1797, when sufficient funds had been raised, a house was rented in Factory Row (now Berry Street). Six bedsteads were purchased, a nurse was appointed and a rota of volunteer doctors was arranged. The venture appears to have been successful, with a high rate of recovery amongst the patients treated – in spite of periodic overcrowding. Sadly, however, when the epidemic subsided the public lost interest in the hospital, and lack of funds forced it to close within the year.

Two years later, however, fever was rife again. Possibly because it was now known that it caused proportionately more deaths amongst the rich than the poor, money was once again forthcoming to provide isolated shelter for fever victims. This time three houses in West Street, off Smithfield, were rented and the Belfast Fever Hospital once more opened its doors, doors which have never since closed.

Within a few years it became apparent that the beds in West Street (to which, fever permitting, medical and surgical cases were also admitted) and in the Charitable Society's poorhouse were just not enough to meet the needs of the rapidly expanding industrial town, particularly during the repeated epidemics. Preparations were made, therefore, to replace the West Street premises with a new hospital, which was built on a site donated by the Marquis of Donegall in Frederick Street – then on the outskirts of the town. The intention was to use thirty of its hundred beds for fever cases and the remainder for general medicine and surgery. However, fever struck again in 1817, and the new hospital had to be rushed into service before the plaster on the walls had dried. For the next twenty years, it was only in the lulls between epidemics that any but the most urgent medical and surgical cases could be admitted. Beds, beds, and yet more beds were demanded for fever victims as epidemic followed epidemic, and as the public came to appreciate more fully the benefits of isolation. Even relatively well-to-do patients were prepared to go into hospital when they contracted fever, either to protect their families or because they had no-one at home to nurse them. The problem was where to find more beds. During epidemics every available space in the hospital was used, but it was still not enough. Although the outbreak of fever in 1831 (probably typhus or typhoid) was the worst since the new hospital had been opened – over 1200 patients were admitted in eighteen months – and it had been complicated at its height by an outbreak of influenza, worse was to come.

In October 1831 word came that cholera was imminent. The course of the epidemic of this dreaded disease – which had never before been seen in Belfast – had been followed with growing apprehension since it had started in Asia in 1830. Now it was on the doorstep. In anticipation of its arrival, cholera wards capable of housing upwards of fifty patients were built at the rear of the hospital. A board of health was also appointed for the town which made detailed preparations for the expected epidemic, including measures to cleanse the streets and lanes and arrangements to quarantine those who came in contact with cholera victims. The epidemic raged from March to December 1832, with 2870 cases in a population of 54,000. The precautions appear to have been effective as the death rate in Belfast was 16 per cent, lower than that in most other large towns.

Fever continued to strike with awful regularity. In 1843, when the supply of beds yet once more failed to meet the demands of an epidemic, a fever shed capable of containing sixty beds was erected in the hospital grounds. It's total inadequacy to meet the ever-growing need was evident within a few weeks when it was found to contain no less than 319 patients!

The first sign of relief for the hospital, in its struggle to cope with the apparently never-ending epidemics, came in 1846, when the Belfast Board of Guardians opened a large fever hospital in the grounds of the union workhouse – the workhouse, with its own infirmary for sick inmates, having been built in 1841.[2]

With the new hospital now equipped to care for the town's fever patients, preparations were made to expand the surgical and medical work in Frederick Street. The building was extended to provide accident wards and bathrooms, and an operating theatre was built beside the surgical wards. This meant that patients for operation no longer had to be carried bodily up and downstairs, a mode of transport understandably rather less than popular with both patients and bearers. The name was also changed from the Belfast Fever Hospital to the Belfast General Hospital.

Unfortunately the plans to alter the emphasis of the work had to be deferred yet again as the town reeled under the impact of the devastating fever epidemic (probably a mixture of typhus and relapsing fever) which followed the potato famine of 1847, when one in four of the population was infected. The hospitals filled to overflowing, then houses were rented and, in the summer, tents erected in the workhouse grounds for seven hundred convalescents. In the General Hospital, non-fever patients were transferred to the cholera wards, and the rest of the beds, including those in the male lock (syphilis) ward, were used for fever victims. In spite of enormous efforts to find enough beds it was often necessary – particularly in June and July 1847, when a staggering 2,348 fever cases were admitted – to put two or even more patients into a bed, and put others on mattresses on the floor.

Although outbreaks of infectious diseases such as dysentery, cholera, influenza, smallpox and measles continued to recur, the 1847 epidemic was the last of such catastrophic proportions and, in 1849, the General Hospital finally ceased to be primarily a fever hospital. A few beds were retained for fever patients who were prepared to pay rather than suffer the stigma of entering the Union Fever Hospital, which they mistakenly believed was part of the workhouse.

Because it was now a general rather than a fever hospital, the annual grant which had been given to it by the Grand Jury for the treatment of fever patients was greatly reduced. As this had been a major source of income, making ends meet, always a problem, became even more difficult. It was not unusual for the Management Committee to be forced to use capital for the day to day work of the hospital, and from time to time funds became so low that closure seemed to be inevitable. Somehow the doors were always kept open, but several times admissions had to be restricted to acute emergencies in order to stave off total bankruptcy. Most accommodation crises were dealt with as they arose, lack of ready money preventing the Committee from making adequate plans in advance.

In an attempt to supplement the income provided by regular (and irregular) subscribers, all patients were asked to contribute to the cost of their treatment if they could. A change in the management structure in 1854 was a thinly disguised means of raising money. The Management Committee was replaced by a much larger general committee, elected from contributors to the hospital funds. Each member of the new Committee then became responsible for fund-raising in a particular area of the town. From the General Committee a board of management was elected to administer the hospital – in effect the Management Committee under a new name!

A monument to philanthropy. The Belfast Fever Hospital, Frederick Street, built for the 'sick poor' on a site donated by the Marquis of Donegal in 1817. (RVH, Belfast)

Those who contributed one guinea or more were also entitled to recommend non-emergency patients for admission. Two such sponsors were required for each patient, but before they were accepted, the Committee had to be satisfied that there was at least some hope that a stay in hospital would be beneficial. The patient had also to give surety (unspecified) that he or she would quit the hospital at the end of the time allotted, unless the doctors felt that a longer stay was necessary.

The ailments of patients admitted to the medical wards of the hospital were frequently the indirect result of poverty, and unhealthy and overcrowded living conditions. An indication of just how unhealthy Belfast was in the nineteenth century was revealed in the 1851 census, when life expectation at birth was estimated to be *nine* years. Rheumatism was common as were chest diseases, particularly bronchitis and tuberculosis, the latter not yet recognised as an infectious disease. Many of those seeking admission were suffering from syphilis, and it is interesting to note that, from time to time, particularly when funds were low, the Management Committee questioned the right of these patients to absorb so much of the hospital's resources, but no satisfactory solution to the problem appears to have been reached.

There was little effective medical treatment in this period. For many – including those suffering from acute rheumatism, nephritis or pneumonia, as well as fever cases – their main hope lay in the cleaner environment of the hospital and in the quality of the nursing care.

When the demands of fever permitted, the surgeons operated for a variety of conditions including different cancers, hernia and cataract, although it was not until the middle of the century that chloroform was available as a general anaesthetic. Perhaps the doctors dulled the pain with opium, the records do not say. They also amputated limbs and trephined skulls. Unfortunately the wounds of these operations almost inevitably became infected, which added greatly to the risk involved. In spite of the use of carbolic acid lotion for washing wounds, the problem of wound infection was not solved until the work of Lister and Pasteur was translated into antiseptic and aseptic surgical techniques in the latter part of the century.

As news of the work being done in the General Hospital spread, the demand for admission to the wards increased, and patients began to come for treatment from outside the town, access to which was now much easier – and more comfortable – since the new railway system had been built. In order to cater for the growing numbers, two new wings were added in 1864-65 through the generosity of local businessmen, Messrs Charters and Mulholland, which increased the number of beds to 160.

For many years the Resident Apothecary took charge of the day to day running of the hospital. A brief and unsuccessful experiment in dual management, when the Apothecary shared his work with a house steward, was followed in 1836 by the appointment of a resident house surgeon, who combined supervision of the hospital with the medical care of the patients, in the absence of the Visiting Medical Staff.

The first hospital in Factory Row employed only one nurse, and the practice for many years was to hire temporary staff as required, dispensing with their services when patient numbers declined. For example, in 1818, when there were over two hundred patients, ten nurses, three menservants, three washerwomen and three kitchen-maids were employed; by 1821, when that particular epidemic had subsided, the staff was reduced to four nurses (of whom two were employed exclusively in the fever wards), one kitchenmaid, one wash-

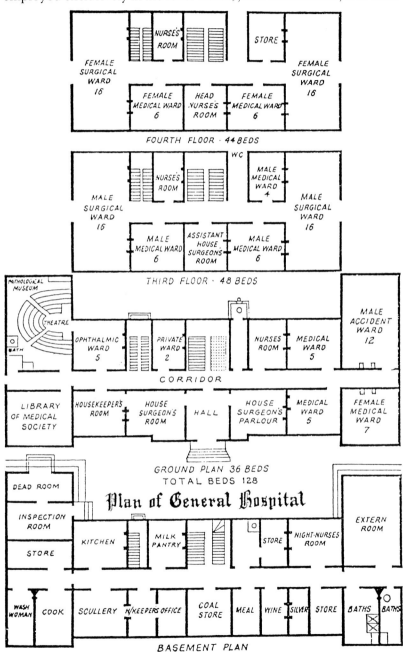

Plan of Belfast General Hospital (c.1850). Although the plan shows nurses' rooms on all floors above ground, they were eventually ousted from there and housed in the dank basement along with the coals, the silverware and the mortuary.
(RVH, Belfast)

erwoman, one housemaid and one porter. Sometimes (usually during epidemics) mothers were allowed to remain in the hospital to nurse their sick children, the Management Committee claiming that they were the natural carers of their offspring at such a time – the fact that it saved on nurses' wages of course being purely incidental! The introduction of automation in the form of flush toilets in 1834 enabled the Management Committee to economise further by paying off two nurses. Convinced that the innovation was a good one – which it undoubtedly was – the Committee was far from pleased to find that the saving in nurses' wages was offset by the frequency with which the services of a plumber were required! The nurses, who did not fully understand the workings of these new-fangled gadgets, attempted to flush quantities of tow down them (toilet paper was still a thing of the future) with the result that they became clogged. They were severely reprimanded because the 'water closets had become deranged through their carelessness', and threatened with dismissal if it happened again.[4]

Occasionally male nurses or attendants were employed. This was usually for the purpose of restraining violent patients, as the doctors strongly advocated the most up-to-date humane treatment of the insane and refused to have them put into strait jackets unless it was absolutely unavoidable.[5]

As their medical expertise grew, the doctors began to appreciate the value of having experienced nurses available, and more were employed on a permanent basis. When the new wings were added to the hospital in 1865, thirteen extra nurses were added to the staff and, by the late 1860s, the regular nursing staff for a thirty-bedded surgical ward was two nurses and two assistant nurses, a similar medical ward having to make do with two nurses and one assistant. Night nurses were employed but there were no wardsmaids, nor were extra nurses available in times of emergency.

The increase in permanent staff led in turn to the foundations being laid for the development of a nursing hierarchy in the hospital. The first step was in the 1820s when head nurses were appointed for each of the different floors or lobbies and the fever wards to supervise the work of the assistant nurses. They were still lowly figures, however, in the overall hospital hierarchy as they were responsible to the doctors for the care of the patients and to the Housekeeper in all other matters.[6] Their humble status was emphasised by the fact that not only was the Resident House Surgeon bound to report their misbehaviours or failings to the Management Committee, but the resident medical students were obliged to do so as well.[7] The next addition to the hierarchical pyramid was in 1832 when Mrs Dobbin, Housekeeper since 1822, retired and it was decided to appoint a head nurse to take charge of nursing throughout the hospital, but who would remain subordinate to the Housekeeper in other matters.

The first holder of this post was a remarkable woman. Ann Marshall was admitted as a patient to West Street in 1810. Her initial two-week stay was extended indefinitely because she made herself so useful in the ward and, when fully recovered, she was taken on as a domestic. In 1812 she was made an assistant nurse, promoted to nurse in 1819, finally becoming Head Nurse in 1832.[8] She remained at work until her death in 1860. As a token of her devotion to the hospital, for many years she made an annual donation of one guinea to its funds out of her fairly meagre pay and, in 1849, when there was yet another financial crisis, also gave it her life savings of £61.9s.10d. After her death she was given the unusual distinction – for a nurse – of having a plaque erected in her honour in the hospital, a bronze copy of which is now in the entrance hall of the nurses' home, Bostock House. It reads:

IN MEMORY OF ANN MARSHALL
WHO FOR UPWARDS OF 50 YEARS
DEVOTED ALL HER SAVINGS
AND ALSO HER VALUED SERVICES
AS MATRON
TO THE BEST INTERESTS OF THIS HOSPITAL
HER FRIENDS DESIRE TO RECORD THEIR OPINION
OF HER UNOSTENTATIOUS PIETY
AND BENEVOLENT EFFORTS
AND OF THE LOSS
THE INSTITUTION HAS SUSTAINED

Died 4th October, 1860   Aged 68 years.
"She hath done what she could".   Mark, XIV, 8

The fact that she was so commemorated is remarkable enough, but the comparatively detailed record of her work in the hospital archives (which, although extensive, are more notable for what they do not tell us about the nurses than for what they do[9]) is an indication of Ann Marshall's undoubted impact upon her contemporaries. Dr Malcolm, a distinguished member of the Visiting Medical Staff, wrote of her in 1851:

This old and respected gentlewoman, after a lapse of 41 years unremitting servitude, still enjoys a wonderful share of health. She may be seen by the visitor making her daily rounds amongst the wards, and with anxious solicitude and a homely care, rendering her little offices to comfort the distressed and the forsaken.[10]

The new Housekeeper, Mrs Gihon, was not altogether happy about sharing her authority with the Head Nurse, and appears to have made her feelings on the subject abundantly clear. She was dismissed in 1841 for spreading rumours about Ann Marshall 'calculated to destroy her authority over the servants',[11] but was reinstated after she had made an abject apology, remaining as Housekeeper until 1855. This antagonism between the Housekeeper and the Head Nurse may have been the reason that the Board of Management decided not to appoint an immediate successor to Ann Marshall in 1860. But, in 1865, when concern about the standard of nursing was being voiced by the doctors, and following the death of Mrs Mewla, Mrs Gihon's successor, it was decided once again to try a head nurse. Mrs Murphy, the nurse in charge of the fever wards, was appointed. Her stay was short. At the end of six months she returned to her former post in the fever wards. No reason for the change is recorded and none appears obvious, particularly as Mrs Murphy continued to receive the pay she had been given as Head Nurse, which was more than her post in the fever wards warranted. It may have had something to do with the personality and capabilities of the new Housekeeper, Mrs Olipherts. With Mrs Murphy's return to the fever wards, responsibility for the nurses reverted once more to the Housekeeper.

The status of the Housekeeper was akin to that of a housekeeper in a private household. In an attempt to ensure that the appointee would give satisfaction, the Committee required a guarantee to this effect from her relatives. A Surgeon Arnott was guarantor for Mrs Dobbin in 1822 to the tune of £50, but the relatives of her successor, Mrs Andrews, in 1832 had to produce £100. Mrs Andrews left the hospital for unknown reasons after only a few months. The records do not reveal what happened to the £100 – a very substantial sum in those days. Applicants in 1869 had not only to be well educated but also be capable of keeping accounts. As the Housekeeper's responsibilities included the general supervision of the nurses in the hospital, it is rather surprising to find no reference to the need for nursing experience in this, or any other, advertisement for the post. Perhaps it was believed that women were born with this knowledge. After all, most sick people were still cared for in their own homes by their female relatives or servants.

To have had experience in home nursing might have been an additional recommendation, but to obtain employment as a nurse in the General Hospital, an applicant had first to produce a good character reference and be able to read and write – skills by no means universal at that time. Only those with experience as assistant nurses were eligible for promotion to the post of nurse. Following interview by the Management Committee, posts were filled and a reserve list compiled. From this list the Housekeeper or Resident House Surgeon filled later vacancies, although all such appointments were temporary until ratified by the Committee.

Conditions of service and pay for the nurses were probably no worse, and possibly even better, than in some of the other available jobs for women. The nurses' bedrooms in the hospital basement in Frederick Street, however, must have been far from comfortable as they periodically became flooded and so were perpetually damp and unhealthy. It was a case of Hobson's choice, however, as they (and presumably also their predecessors in West Street and Factory Row) had to 'live in'.

Their food was adequate and filling but, by modern standards, dull in the extreme! In 1828 their daily menu was:

Breakfast	1 quart stirabout
	1 quart sour milk
Dinner	$^1/_2$ lb beef
	1 pint soup
	3 lbs potatoes
Supper	1 pint stirabout or flummery
	1 pint sour or $^1/_2$ pint sweet milk

A tea ration was an important addition, and the misappropriation of it by a dishonest housekeeper in the 1820s led to complaints being made by nurses and servants to the Committee. To save any further trouble a small increase in pay was substituted for the tea. Rations were distributed twice weekly, and the nurses cooked and ate their own food in the ward kitchen. The Housekeeper and the Resident House Surgeon were given a daily allowance of ale, but it was apparently not considered appropriate (or wise?) to give any to the nurses.

Nearly forty years later, the diet had improved, but only slightly. In the mid 1860s the nurses' weekly rations comprised:

Tea	$3^1/_2$ oz
Sugar	1 lb
Bread	6 lbs
Butter	$^1/_2$ lb
Beef	$3^1/_2$ lbs
Sweetmilk	$3^1/_2$ pints
Sour milk	$3^1/_2$ pints
Soap	$^1/_2$ lb [12]

The soap ration was to allow the nurses to do their own laundry. At first they appear to have had to provide their working clothes, but from about 1860 the hospital gave them bonnets and jackets for use on duty. There are no surviving pictures – if any were ever taken – of the General Hospital nurses, but photographs taken in other hospitals suggest that the bonnets were white cotton or linen and the jackets short, tightfitting, dark and possibly made of serge or a similar woollen material. Dresses were protected with an all-enveloping white apron.

At first all nurses were paid at the same rate of 6d. (2¹/₂p) a week, raised in 1824 to 8d. In 1826, following the protest over the tea allowance, a rate of 2s.6d. (12¹/₂p) was introduced for temporary, experienced nurses, and 2s.0d. a week for assistants. The rates were gradually increased, and by 1870 a regular nurse in charge of a department was receiving 6s.0d. a week, the same pay as a parlour-maid, although the latter did not have to be able to read and write. Night nurses were paid slightly more than day staff. The most poorly paid of all were the lock ward nurses who received about half the wages of assistant nurses in other wards. The nurses' wages were undoubtedly small and, in mid-century, on a par with those of women working in the linen mills. Unlike the mill-workers, however, they had free board and lodging. The Housekeeper, who in 1818 received £20 a year, had her pay increased by 1860 to £40, and to £60 five years later. When Ann Marshall was appointed Head Nurse she was paid £10 a year; this was later increased to £11.5s., with an additional 1s.0d. a week during epidemics. Because nursing in the fever wards was known to be more dangerous than in the medical and surgical wards, fever nurses were paid slightly higher wages. After particularly severe epidemics they were often given bonuses as well.

In 1858 bonuses for long service with good conduct were introduced for all nurses, £2 extra a year being given (on Christmas Day) for ten years' service, and £1 for five to ten years' service. There were other occasional extras such as the 1s.6d. a week paid from 1869 for attending female patients in the Turkish baths. Some nurses tried to supplement their wages by doing embroidery for outside employers – a practice specifically forbidden by the Management.

Nurses had no financial security; it was generally a case of no work, no pay, and their wages did not leave much over to provide for times of unemployment or for old age. They often worked on long after they were unfit to do so, either because of advancing years or illness

If pay was short, hours of duty were not, and limited off-duty gave little opportunity for spending wages – a reason perhaps why Ann Marshall was able to accumulate her nest-egg. Day assistant nurses were on duty at 6 a.m., more senior staff at 7 a.m., both remaining on duty until 10 p.m. Twice a week, on Sunday, Tuesday or Thursday –

Official issue. Nurses were first issued with uniform bonnets and jackets in the 1850s. The uniform has always kept abreast of fashion, and this style was then all the rage.

provided that the Visiting Surgeon or Physician had completed his rounds – they were allowed off duty at 2 p.m. Night nurses were on duty from 10 p.m. to 7 a.m.

Not only were the nurses' off duty hours brief but their activities in their free time were also restricted by many rules and regulations. They were forbidden to bring visitors into their rooms, so could only meet friends or relatives, including children (in these years most nurses were either married or widows) at the hospital gate, and then only at certain specified times. If a nurse wanted to go out in her off-duty she had first to get written permission from the Apothecary or Resident House Surgeon *and* the Housekeeper, then had to be back by 9 p.m. in winter and 9.45 p.m. in summer. The Housekeeper was allowed visitors in her apartments – but was strictly forbidden to hold parties!

In 1836, off-duty hours were changed to enable half the nurses to attend worship (compulsorily!) on alternate Sunday mornings and evenings. This innovation may have been an attempt to reinforce moral standards, as it followed a recent scandal in the hospital when a nurse, against all the rules, had become rather too friendly with a medical student and as a result had departed 'in a state of preg-nancy'.[13]

Penalties for other misdemeanours varied. For some a reprimand by the Management Committee was considered sufficient. This was the corrective used for nurses who did not treat the doctors with due respect. In 1865, Ellen Burns, the nurse in charge of the top lobby, was severely reprimanded for drunkenness. It must be assumed, in the light of the relatively mild punishment for a recurring offence, that she was otherwise a satisfactory member of staff. For more serious of-fences there were fines or dismissal. For throwing bandages in the dust heap in 1860 a nurse was fined 6d., and an assistant nurse 3d. Others were dismissed for persistent rule-breaking, absenting them-selves without leave, inefficiency, or for harshness to patients – the rules specifically requiring nurses to treat patients with kindness and tenderness. (Appendix A)

Apart from Ellen Burns, there is relatively little reference in the records to drunkenness amongst the nurses. Indeed when the risks incurred by them during the epidemics of the nineteenth century are appreciated, the need occasionally for a little Dutch courage is under-standable. Although it was realised that there was a link between dirt and disease, and that boiling somehow got rid of contagion, there was no real understanding of how fevers or tuberculosis (rampant in nineteenth century Belfast) spread, and the records often tell of nurses

A hospital on the move. Map of Belfast showing the sites of the first version of the Royal in Factory Row (now Berry Street), its second home in West Street (off Smithfield) and its first custom-built premises in Frederick Street – then on the outskirts of the town.

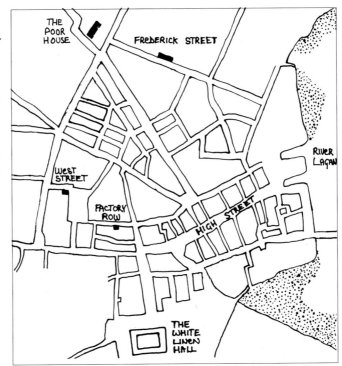

catching fever – and dying of it. In 1848 the entire nursing staff was struck down, and both the Resident House Surgeon and his assistant died from fever; and in 1865 it also caused the death of the House-keeper, Mrs Mewla. The minutes pay frequent tribute to the nurses' courage and devotion to duty during epidemics. There was praise too for all the hospital staff in 1864, when a week of violent sectarian rioting in the town brought a huge influx of patients to the hospital (75 admissions and as many more outpatients) for treatment of various injuries, including gunshot wounds – shades of things to come.

Epidemics and riots provided dramatic highlights in a day to day routine that was hard and often monotonous. Much of it was domestic, particularly for the assistant nurses, so it is no surprise to find that, during most of the nineteenth century, their status was akin to that of the lower domestics. (Some assistant nurses even applied for jobs as domestic servants.) They had to wash the ward floors and stairs daily and the patients' dishes after each meal. In the days before bathrooms and flush toilets, they had to carry the 'slops' and rubbish out to the yard for disposal. In the opposite direction they had to carry water, food and coal to the wards – no mean task in a three-storey building without lifts, and by candlelight at night before 1840, when gas lighting was installed. (One can sympathise with those nurses who, tired of toiling up and down stairs, threw their rubbish out of the windows into the grounds of the adjoining Ragged School![14])

Patients as well as wards had to be kept clean. Each one had his or her hands and face washed on admission and daily thereafter. Personal and bed linen were changed regularly, as was the straw in the mattresses before the introduction of hair mattresses and waterproof sheets in the mid 1860s.

The more experienced nurses were also responsible for giving out medicines and applying poultices – linseed being particularly favoured – but not, at first, for doing surgical dressings. In later years this task was taken over by the nurses, but officially only if done under the supervision of a doctor or medical student – although one house surgeon in 1864 admitted that nurses were often better at doing dressings than the majority of doctors! The nurse in charge at the end of each day gave a report to the incoming night nurse on the condition of the patients in the ward and on the treatment they had been given. In the morning the night nurse in turn reported on any changes which had taken place overnight.

There is little doubt that to have been a nurse in the Belfast General Hospital, or in its predecessors, was not easy. The hours were long, the pay small and the work both hard and, at times, dangerous. There were those, however, who accepted it as at least a tolerable means of livelihood, possibly less onerous than mill work, and infinitely better than being unemployed in an era when no work meant no pay. Some spent many years in the service of the hospital and earned the respect of the doctors for whom they worked. One such was Ann Marshall, whose unusually well documented record clearly shows that not all nurses of the pre-Nightingale era were Sairey Gamps. Another long-serving nurse was Lizzie Hanna, who was appointed as an assistant nurse in 1868 and two years later was put in charge of the Extern Department. In that post she was remembered by Dr R.J.Johnstone (later to become a distinguished member of the Visiting Medical Staff of the hospital) as:

Great, physically, mentally and temperamentally. She sat in the front entrance of the waiting hall, beside the bandage winder, from where she ran the whole Extern, Visiting Staff, house surgeons, students, nurses, patients and all. No one dared dispute her authority.[15]

In 1870, the doctors were still unhappy about what they felt was an unsatisfactory standard of nursing in the hospital. It may have been that the new popular image of nursing, which had developed following the publicity given to Florence Nightingale and her work in the Crimea, had persuaded them that higher standards were both possible and desirable. No-one knows. What we do know is that the nurses of the Belfast General Hospital were poised to enter the Nightingale era. The doctors wanted something done about the nursing? Something was just about to be done.

2   The Nightingale Era 1870 – 1903

In 1875 another milestone was reached when the hospital was granted a Royal charter and was renamed the Belfast Royal. If one of the reasons for seeking the charter was a hope that it would raise the status of the hospital in the eyes of the public and so increase the number of contributors, the Board must have been disappointed as, within two years of its re-christening, the hospital was again quite heavily overdrawn at the bank. Its financial problems were compounded not only by the prevailing economic depression but by the opening in Belfast of a number of small specialist hospitals and a second general hospital – the Mater Infirmorum – all of which were also supported entirely by voluntary contributions.[1] In spite of all the difficulties, however, as there was still a growing demand for hospital treatment in the town, it was decided to plan a new hospital rather than try to make do with what, by the 1890s, had become over-crowded and out-of-date accommodation. Smoke pollution and poor drainage made further building in Frederick Street inadvisable, so it was decided to look for a site elsewhere. A campaign was launched in 1897 to raise funds for a new hospital to commemorate the Diamond Jubilee of Queen Victoria. A second Royal charter was obtained, permitting the addition of the Queen's name to the title. In spite of the claims of the other hospitals, enough money was collected to enable the project to go ahead, and work began on a site on Grosvenor Street (now Grosvenor Road) in the grounds of the District Lunatic Asylum.

Meantime, the work in Frederick Street continued to expand. Although no further major additions were made to the buildings after the new wings were added in the 1860s, by reorganising the existing accommodation the number of beds was increased to 196 by the end of the century. Two new specialist departments were also established, for gynaecology and for eye, ear, nose and throat diseases. The Throne Children's Hospital and adjoining land were given to the hospital in 1875, and a much needed convalescent home was opened on the site two years later.

The number of beds in constant occupation increased steadily – by 1890 it was about 140 and by 1900 had reached 161. The reason for this was four-fold; firstly, the continuing growth of the population; secondly, the increasing range of surgical operations, particularly abdominal surgery, now possible because antiseptic and aseptic techniques greatly reduced the risk of peritonitis as well as wound infection; thirdly, the expansion in local industry which brought a rising toll of casualties from the factories, mills and shipyards, where safety regulations were largely a thing of the future; and finally, the ever-increasing volume of road traffic. Towards the end of the twentieth century it is difficult to visualise serious road accidents being caused by horse-drawn vehicles, but a recklessly driven ginger-beer or bread cart, particularly on wet cobbles or square setts, could be every bit as lethal as a modern lorry.

Adam Macrory, solicitor, churchman, philanthropist and nursing visionary. Honorary Secretary of the Belfast General Hospital 1860-79. (R.W.M.Strain, Belfast and its Charitable Society)

Apart from the perennial difficulty of money, the main problem facing the Board of Management in 1870 was what to do about improving the standard of nursing in the hospital. The doctors had been worried for some time about the increasing frequency of serious mishaps such as that of November 1870 when, during an epidemic, assistant nurses who were looking after surgical patients were sent to help clean the smallpox wards; unfortunately they carried the infection back with them to the surgical wards and a number of their patients developed smallpox. What could be done to prevent such a thing happening again? Would it be a good idea to reintroduce a head nurse? No-one seemed sure. Then, in December 1870, another solution was offered.

At the Annual General Meeting of subscribers, the Honorary Secretary, Mr Adam Macrory, proposed that the hospital should open a nurse training school. It would, he suggested, not only provide trained nurses for the hospital, but also nurses for the sick poor in their own homes. He had been interested in nurse training since a visit some years earlier to King's College Hospital in London where nurses were trained under the auspices of St John's House. More recently he had seen the new training school in Liverpool in action and been very impressed by it. Now, with nurse training very much in the public eye since the opening, in 1860, of the Nightingale School of Nursing in St Thomas's Hospital, London, it seemed that the time was ripe to introduce a similar system in Belfast. The proposal was very well received, and the meeting voted unanimously to ask the Board to prepare plans.

During the following months the alternative methods of organising a training school were examined by the Board – with the bulk of the work apparently being done by Adam Macrory himself (he was also a practising solicitor). He did a grand tour of most of the hospitals and nurses' homes throughout the United Kingdom where training schemes had already been established, most of them based on the St Thomas's pattern. Of them all he preferred Liverpool, where a nurses' training school had been set up in association with the Royal Infirmary. The plan that was presented at the next annual general meeting in November 1871 was based on this pattern.

It proposed that a nurses' home and training school should be set up in association with, but independent of, the hospital and its Board.[2] Nurses would obtain their practical experience in the hospital but would live in a separate nurses' home. The ladies of its Board of Management would supervise the day to day running of the home and select candidates for training.

Although Adam Macrory – a devout Christian with a strong social conscience[3] – had originally suggested that any nurses trained in the home who were not needed in the hospital should be made available for nursing the sick poor in their own houses, the new plan had a different aim. It proposed that the surplus nurses should be used for private work, not for the poor. The records do not explain why this change was made, but it may have been at the suggestion of the doctors on the Board who, when they required a nurse to attend a private patient in his or her home, often had to bring one from as far afield as Dublin or England.[4] There appear to have been a few private nurses in Belfast at this time, but not enough to meet the demand. On the other hand the economic benefits of a private nursing service could not be overlooked if the proposed home was to be financially independent. Whatever the reason, this plan was accepted.

When established, the home was to take over the nursing in the hospital, and would be paid £40 a year for each trained nurse employed. No payment would be made for nurses in training (probationers) who would obtain their necessary practical experience by sharing the work on the wards. The home would provide board, lodging and laundry, and pay salaries: first year probationers receiving £15, rising by £1 for each of the following two years. Trained staff would be paid a little over £20 a year.

The oldest known photograph of Royal nurses. A recently qualified group pose in their new uniforms in 1895. Marianne Harden, front left, is the nurse whose abiding memory of hospital life was of endless floor scrubbing. (Miss A. Flack, Glenanne)

A lady superintendent would take charge of both hospital and private nursing; she would also be responsible for training the probationers. A matron would be employed to supervise the general housekeeping in the home. Probationers (who would be selected by the

Ladies' Committee) had to be between twenty-five and thirty-five years old and able to read and write. A limited number of ladies (the records give no detail as to what constituted a lady in this context) should they offer, would be received into the home and be trained for nursing in private families. In spite of repeated pleas, however, there is no evidence of any such ladies ever having applied.

The probationer's contract with the home would be for three years, of which the first year only would be spent in training, when each probationer would spend time in both medical and surgical wards. There would be opportunity for the doctors to lecture but, at this preliminary stage, lectures appear to have been considered an optional extra. The second and third years would be spent working for the home, either in the hospital or as a private nurse. If, at the end of the third year, her moral conduct was considered satisfactory, she would be given a testimonial as a qualified nurse. There appears to have been no need to prove herself as a nurse!

Although the hospital was to give the home a rent-free house for its first year, it was eventually to become financially independent. It was hoped that the profits from private nursing (when enough trained nurses were available) would provide most of the necessary income.

No time was lost. The Board of Management was appointed in December 1871. At its first meeting the Honorary Secretary, Miss Minnie Otway, was asked to write to Florence Nightingale – nothing less than the best would do! – for advice on setting up the home and help in finding a suitable lady superintendent.

Miss Otway duly wrote, enclosing a copy of the prepared constitution of the home for Miss Nightingale's comments (Appendix B). Her reply was almost certainly lost with the rest of the home's records in the Belfast air raids of 1941, but her notes on her copy of the constitution survive (Appendix C). She objected strongly to the amount of authority accorded to the Ladies Committee, one of the mainstays of her nurse training system being that absolute authority over the nurses should be solely in the hands of a lady superintendent or matron.[5] She was also strongly disapproving of the suggestion that the nurses from the home should be employed in private work, commenting in the margin of the constitution:

"Lady" pupils will *never* take "Private" nursing and ought not if they would.[6]

Not surprisingly, there was opposition by the Medical Staff to the proposal that a lady superintendent should be given overall control of the nurses, as this had previously been their prerogative. (Male chauvinism was alive and flourishing in Victorian Belfast!) They also objected to the proposal that the nurses should live in comfortable quarters away from the hospital wards. Why could they not stay right where they were in the damp basement, where they were easily available if needed?

The guardian of the household? This formidable lady, pictured c. 1900, is almost certainly Mrs Waters, Housekeeper of the Frederick Street hospital from 1887 to 1901, when she was replaced by Miss M.F. Bostock. (RVH, Belfast)

After much discussion, and in spite of Florence Nightingale's remonstrations and recommendations, a compromise was reached. Before any new nurse was placed in a ward the physician or surgeon in charge would be consulted, and the doctors would retain overall authority over both the nurses and the Lady Superintendent, up to, and including, the power of dismissal. In order to retain an illusion of her supposed authority, the act of dismissing a nurse would, however, be carried out by the Lady Superintendent. It was also conceded that, although most of the trained nurses and all the probationers would be housed in the home, three of the senior nurses would continue to live in the hospital. In return for these very substantial concessions, the hospital Board rather parsimoniously agreed that the Lady Superintendent should be allowed to take over the Housekeeper's responsibilities relating to the nursing staff – the Housekeeper herself neither being included in the discussion nor consulted on the matter!

While the negotiations with the hospital were going on, Miss Otway was also seeking advice from Mrs Wardroper, Matron of St Thomas's Hospital and head of the Nightingale School of Nursing, and with Mr Bonham Carter, Secretary of the Nightingale Fund,[7] in an unsuccessful attempt to find a suitable Lady Superintendent.

Meantime, Miss Merryweather, Lady Superintendent of the Liverpool Nurses Home and Training School, who had spent a short time studying the new Nightingale system in St Thomas's before opening the Liverpool school in 1862, was invited to Belfast to assist with plans and to help with fund-raising. She was also invited back to help launch the home, which opened in May, 1872 at No.2 Frederick Street. She brought with her three of her trained nurses from the Infirmary to help teach the first probationers.

The opening of the home brought major changes in the hospital as responsibility for the nursing care of the patients was transferred. Assistant nurses were dispensed with, some of them probably becoming domestics, as extra wardsmaids were employed to relieve the nurses of the heavier cleaning chores. While the modern trade unionist might raise his or her hands in horror at this apparent demotion, the change in the work they had to do was minimal – if, indeed, there was any change at all. Their pay was probably no different. Other nurses on the staff were given the option of undertaking the new training which, it was believed, would greatly improve their future employment prospects. If they did this, they nominally became probationers but were often given responsibility in keeping with their known and recognised ability; if they did not, they were kept on, but were paid at a lower rate than those trained under the new system.

Miss Merryweather returned to Liverpool after three weeks and Miss Persse, who had trained in Liverpool, was appointed as the first Lady Superintendent of the Belfast Nurses Home and Training School. At her own request she spent her first holiday at St Thomas's in order to familiarize herself with the Nightingale method at first hand. Her sister joined her as Matron of the home.

Doctors' lectures commenced after the first six months, but attendance at them was not compulsory until 1890 and, for a time, in the 1880s they were abandoned altogether – the doctors at that time apparently considering them unnecessary for the training of nurses. Nursing, hygiene, and later invalid cookery were taught by the Lady Superintendent. Examinations were first held in 1890 and training certificates were given to successful candidates when they completed their three-year contract.

If a nurse broke her contract she was fined heavily. One who left in 1892 'to marry clandestinely' had to pay £20,[8] and six years later the fine for the same offence had been raised to £30 – heavy indeed when one realises that the total earnings of the nurses for the initial three-year period were at that time only £33. The practice of paying first year probationers had been stopped some years earlier, as an economy measure.

In 1896 the training was increased to two years and the contract period to three and a half. Probationers were charged a premium of £10 to help defray the extra cost of their extended stay in the home.

When the nurses finished their contract they had little difficulty in

A rare glimpse of the Belfast Nurses Home in a photograph by A.R.Hogg (1930s). Hogg seems to have been more interested in the workmen sitting beside the brazier with their sandwiches than in the Home, most of which is out of frame to the right. (Hogg Collection, Ulster Museum)

finding jobs. Trained nurses were still relatively scarce and were much in demand, as private nurses, in the district nursing services of the Belfast Society for Providing Nurses for the Sick Poor and Queen Victoria's Jubilee Institute of District Nursing, and in other voluntary hospitals and Poor Law Union infirmaries.

With good employment prospects there was no shortage of applicants for training, and the home accepted an increasing number of probationers. As the hospital was only able to accommodate about twenty of them each year, provision had to be made for some to get part of their practical experience in hospitals elsewhere in the United Kingdom.

The premises at No.2 Frederick Street were not even big enough to house the hospital nurses and probationers, never mind the private nurses whose income was essential if the home was to become self-sufficient. The adjoining house was rented, but this was still not enough so; with Florence Nightingale's encouragement, plans were made to build a new home opposite the hospital.(Appendix D) It opened in 1875 at No. 32 Frederick Street. Four storeys high, and towering over the adjoining buildings, it not only provided room for more private nurses but also enabled nurses to be accepted for training in district work for the Belfast Society for Providing Nurses for the Sick Poor – happily fulfilling the second, more philanthropic, of Adam Macrory's original aims for the home.

Although the increase in income from private nursing was welcome, it was not enough to make the home independent as long as it remained tied to the hospital. It was apparent from an early stage that there was no profit to be made in providing nurses for the hospital. On the contrary, this side of its work was putting the home into debt! After much haggling the hospital Board was persuaded to increase its annual payment for each nurse from £40 to £45, and eventually, in 1900, to make a contribution of £15 a year towards the upkeep of probationers as well.

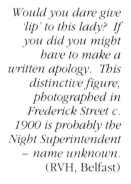

Would you dare give 'lip' to this lady? If you did you might have to make a written apology. This distinctive figure, photographed in Frederick Street c. 1900 is probably the Night Superintendent – name unknown.
(RVH, Belfast)

The financial disagreements were but one facet of the bad relations that soured the association between the home and the hospital for over thirty years. If one judges those relations solely on their annual reports, it would appear that they were extremely cordial, as each, with monotonous and dutiful regularity, praises the other's work. In reality, however, this was far from the truth. From the beginning there was discord between the two Boards, in spite of the fact that a number of men served on both, and that several members of the Ladies' Committee were relatives of men on the hospital Board.

There were also clashes between the Lady Superintendents and the hospital Housekeepers, who resented the removal of their traditional authority over the nurses. In spite of early enthusiasm for the new scheme, some doctors felt that the Lady Superintendent had been given too much power, even though it was less than that given to her counterparts in many English hospitals.

Many of the disagreements were very petty. When the home complained about the poor state of the hospital mattresses, the hospital refused to do anything about them, insisting that they were perfectly satisfactory. On another occasion, the Night Superintendent was refused admission to a ward by a resident medical student. At other times the disputes were over major issues, one of which led to the resignation of the first Lady Superintendent, few of whom could stand the pressure for long. (In the first fifteen years of the home's existence there were no less than eight holders of this post).

Miss Persse resigned in June 1874 following a move by the hospital to reclaim some of its lost authority over the nursing staff. The Board, without consulting anybody, issued new rules for the Resident House Surgeon, which included one stating:

He shall have the power, with the concurrence of the Orderly or one of the Medical Staff, or the Housekeeper, of fining or dismissing any of the nurses or servants for neglect or improper conduct.[9]

This was, in effect, a reversion to the rules of 1832 and it infuriated both the Ladies Committee and Miss Persse. In her resignation letter she wrote:

The interest of the Home and my own self-respect demand it, knowing how impossible it would be efficiently to discharge my duties without control over those serving under me.[10]

The row simmered on, and in October of the following year Miss Otway appealed to Mr Bonham Carter at the Nightingale Fund for help – apparently to no avail. (Appendix E) In December the dispute finally boiled over into the columns of the local press. An acrimonious letter from Miss Otway was published in response to an anonymous letter which had accused the home of interfering in the hospital's affairs. Miss Otway claimed that the hospital had rewritten the agreed rules without consulting the home, and wrote bitterly:

It strikes me that this has all arisen from the hospital Board forgetting they they have given up having any nurses of their own.

Her parting shot to the anonymous writer was:

Anyone who could and wished to make such a statement should have done it

A woman of consequence. A ward sister in the Royal Victoria Hospital, Frederick Street c.1900. By the end of the century the title of sister had been introduced for the nurses in charge of the different floors or departments. (RVH, Belfast)

in a straightforward manner, *giving their name.*

The following day a letter was published from Mr H.H.McNeile of Parkmount, a member of the Committee of the home, expressing regret over Miss Otway's 'hostile correspondence' which he considered to be 'ill-timed, unwise and to be regretted'.[11] With ill-will clearly evident within the ranks of the Management Committee of the home as well as between the home and the hospital, perhaps the outspoken Miss Otway was wise to resign.

When Miss Persse resigned she was succeeded by one of the surgical sisters, Miss Ada Bourne. Miss Bourne, who had trained in St Thomas's, appears to have been on very good terms with both the doctors and with the hospital Board as, shortly after her appointment as Lady Superintendent, she was asked to help find a replacement for an unsatisfactory housekeeper. While the squabble over the new rule continued, Miss Bourne seems to have managed to rise above it, and when she resigned in December 1875, in anticipation of her marriage to Dr (later Sir) William Whitla, she sent a letter of appreciation to the hospital Board, which in turn passed a resolution of appreciation for her work 'for so long a time'.[12] She had been in office less than two years!

Another member of the staff, Miss Kennedy, temporarily filled the post until Miss Nottcutt was appointed early in 1876. Miss Nottcutt had been a ward sister in St Thomas's following her training there, but was unpopular with the surgeon because of her 'surgical awkwardness'.[13]

For Mrs Wardroper (the Matron of St Thomas's) and Miss Nightingale, who were reluctant to dismiss her from her post, believing this would cause her undue distress, the vacancy in Belfast must have been a godsend. Fortunately, Miss Nottcutt appears to have been more successful as Lady Superintendent than she had been as a surgical sister, and she remained in the post until 1881 when she resigned through ill-health.

Miss Nottcutt was succeeded by a Miss Townson or Townsend. In marked contrast to her predecessor, Miss Townson appears to have clashed frequently with the hospital Board, and particularly with the doctors on it. (Perhaps this was the reason that no great effort was made to get her name correct in the records!) She was concerned that her probationers should receive proper training, and not just be exploited as cheap labour; but, in allocating her nurses where they would get good experience, she sometimes failed to ensure that they would not at the same time risk spreading infection. She sent nurses from the surgical wards to the isolation ward to help with dressing infected wounds and, at least once, the returning nurses carried infection with them, just as they had in 1870. (The doctors must have wondered at these times if any progress had been made at all with the new regime.) Miss Townson again came into conflict with the doctors when she removed a nurse from the hospital to look after a private case outside – although the doctors themselves were in the habit of

Mistress of all she surveys. Miss Lydia Newman, Lady Superintendent of the Belfast Nurses Home 1886-1928. Unintimidated by what was acknowledged to be a very difficult job, she survived, indeed flourished, where many of her predecessors had fallen by the wayside. (RVH, Belfast)

doing the same thing! Altogether it was an unhappy association, and when Miss Townson tendered her resignation in 1884 the doctors refused to give her a testimonial until she had left the hospital.

The same Miss Kennedy who had acted as a stop-gap in 1874 was appointed to replace Miss Townson, but remained for only a year, and little is known about her. Her successor, Miss Grace Hartley, was only in office eight months when ill-health forced her to retire. Miss Byam, appointed in November 1885, lasted an even shorter time but, when she resigned in February 1886, she recommended Miss Lydia Newman, from St Marylebone Infirmary, for the post.

It was decided to invite Miss Newman, who had trained in St Bartholomew's Hospital, London, to take the vacant position of Night Superintendent as a trial before considering her for the post of Lady Superintendent. The trial was apparently satisfactory and Miss Newman was duly appointed, becoming the first Lady Superintendent to serve for more than four years. In fact she remained with the home until 1928, and a few elderly nurses remember her as a rather aloof lady who still retained a marked English accent. Although she applied for several other posts, she was always persuaded to stay, and in 1893, as an extra inducement, her annual salary was raised to £100.

About the time of Miss Newman's appointment, the hospital Board decided that it was time to try and find some solution to what had become an almost intolerable situation. Annoyed by yet another request from the home for an increase in payment for its services, the Board began to make enquiries about the cost of nursing in other hospitals where the board of management was directly responsible for both nursing service and training. No immediate action was taken, but, in 1894 the Medical Staff was asked to report on the general administration of the hospital, and particularly on the nursing service. Its report condemned, 'The objectionable system of dual control which at present exists', and recommended that, in future, all nursing and housekeeping duties should be carried out by one individual.[14] It was considered wiser to wait until the hospital transferred to new premises before making any change, so nothing was done until 1901 when, in anticipation of the move to Grosvenor Street, a matron, who was also a trained nurse, was appointed to combine these two offices. The age of the modern matron had arrived.

In 1903 the contract between the home and the hospital was ended, with an agreement that nurses already in training should be allowed to complete their courses in the new hospital – for a fee of course!

The home continued as a private nursing agency until 1941, when it was destroyed in the German air-raids on Belfast, along with its written records.[15] Its former site is now a car park, but a few cracked and discoloured hall floor tiles mark the spot where it once stood.

*High fashion 1890s
style, showing the
then current 'leg o'
mutton' sleeves.*

The story of the hospital and its nurses in this period tends to be dominated by the power struggle, which continued virtually throughout their association, between the Boards of the hospital and the home and, to a lesser extent, between the Lady Superintendents and the doctors. It is difficult to judge, at this distance and with incomplete records, who was the winner. Perhaps neither side. It is hoped that the patients were not the losers.

What about the nurses who were caring for the patients while the battle raged above them? Did the dispute filter down to their lowly level? There is no evidence to suggest that it affected them to any great extent. But it was a period of great change for them, much of it for the better. They were getting a certificated training which qualified them for employment in hospitals as far afield as Australia and the United States (some of them as hospital matrons). For a few there was the opportunity to obtain specialist theatre nursing experience because, as the number of operations had increased, a nurse had been employed solely for this work – an arrangement which proved to be so satisfactory that, in 1899, a full-time theatre sister was appointed. By 1899 training in Weir Mitchell massage was available to the nurses (no details are recorded as to who taught it or where), and a number were sent to St Thomas's for extra courses (content unspecified).

The accommodation in the nurses' home, where each trained nurse had her own bedroom (probationers often had to share), was very much better than that provided earlier in the hospital basement. They also had regular holidays and a monthly day off and, in addition to board, lodging and laundry, a full outdoor and indoor uniform was provided from 1890, replacing the previously issued bonnet and jacket. The new, washable, uniform of a dark cotton dress, white apron, cuffs and cap – variations in the latter, and in the colour of dress, distinguishing the different ranks in the nursing hierarchy – was unpopular at first, even though it was styled in the current fashion with large 'leg o' mutton' sleeves.

Although pay increased only slightly, pensions were provided for all nurses from a fund started in 1872 with a donation of £60.9s., the proceeds of a concert in the Theatre Royal, Belfast, by the 76th Highlanders. This fund – which, for example, provided Nurse Conn with a pension of £26 a year when she retired in 1898 after twenty-five years in charge of the fever wards – was very important, as it promised at least a modicum of security in old age. The pension fund remained with the nurses in the home after its partnership with the hospital ended in 1903, and Royal Victoria Hospital nurses were left without an assured pension until the 1930s.[16]

It always helps to have a friend. Two probationers in the Frederick Street hospital c. 1900, their 'tweeny' style mob caps perhaps indicative both of their lowly status and their domestic workload.
(RVH, Belfast)

There were improvements from the patients' point of view as well. With a larger permanent staff, and extra nurses available in times of emergency, standards of care were easier to maintain. Certainly, new regulations which required patients to be bathed on admission (in bed if necessary) and regularly thereafter, were an improvement – if the regulations were always adhered to; complaints from the Throne Hospital about the dirty state of transferred patients suggest that they were not. Nor, to judge from patients' complaints about being wakened for washing early in the morning, was this new enthusiasm for cleanliness universally popular among the intended beneficiaries.

There was still, however, an element of *plus ça change plus c'est la même chose.* In spite of the introduction of wardsmaids, probationer nurses continued to do most of the heavy domestic work. In the 1890s, the mother of one complained to the Board about the amount of carrying up and down stairs her daughter had to do and, in later years, another probationer's most vivid memory of her training days (also in the 1890s) was of the unpopular, and seemingly endless, chore of floor scrubbing.[17] While the original intention had been to reduce the amount of domestic work done by the nurses in training, the need for strict economy, combined with the fact that first year probationers cost the hospital nothing while domestic servants had to be paid, led to a reduction in the number of wardsmaids employed for work which probationers could do.

Also, and quite inexcusably, mistakes were still being made which led to unnecessary suffering. Nurses were still being sent from nursing infectious cases to the surgical wards, with disasterous results and, even as late as 1898, a badly burned woman was put into the same bed as a child with skin disease – not Miss Newman's fault this time as she was on holiday, and was presumably furious on her return to discover what had happened.

All told, the period 1872 to 1903, while bringing many changes for all nurses, was most difficult for the Lady Superintendents. The Nightingale system, or at least the hospital's version of it, was not the

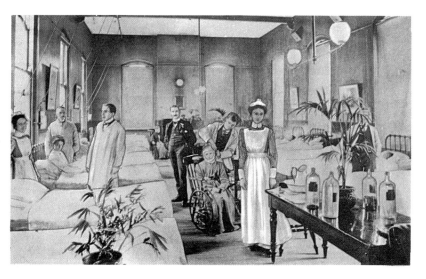

'And where is the patient nurse?' A ward in the Royal Victoria Hospital, Frederick Street, c.1900. The doctor in the foreground beside the empty bed is Dr T.S. Logan, uncle of Dr J.S. Logan, later a member of the Visiting Medical Staff of the hospital and now Honorary Archivist. The dark-suited figure is the Dispenser, Mr Cole. (RVH, Belfast)

success that had been anticipated. This was primarily because of the tenacious unwillingness on the part of the doctors and the hospital Board to relinquish their traditional authority over the nurses, but also because the Lady Superintendent, who was responsible for supervising the work of the nurses in the hospital wards, was not a member of the hospital staff. Rather surprisingly, there is no evidence that this status was ever sought for, or by, her. But there is little doubt that, because she was regarded as 'one of them' rather than 'one of us', she received little co-operation and at times appears to have been deliberately isolated.

Although it failed, the experiment left a number of legacies, some good, others less so. Firstly, it introduced an organised system of certificated and examined training; secondly, it established the principle that nurses should be housed away from the wards in a nurses' home; thirdly, it brought – albeit reluctantly – a recognition by both the doctors and Board that the most appropriate person to organise and supervise nursing was the head nurse, be she called lady superintendent or matron. On the negative side, the experience of Frederick Street led, for many years, to this authority being limited to a greater extent than in many other hospitals. Although it was common practice for matrons to attend management meetings when nursing matters were discussed, this did not happen in the Royal until the 1960s. Before then, Matron could only communicate her requests or give her opinion (if asked!) at first through the medium of the Board's Nursing Sub-committee and later through the Medical Superintendent. Finally, and also on the negative side, the pattern was established in the Royal, as in all other hospitals where nurse training schemes were introduced, of using the probationers as the mainstay of the nursing service, as well as for much of the domestic work of the wards. This was not because either was regarded as essential for the probationer's training, but because it had been found to be the most economical, and indeed possibly the only, way of maintaining a service in a hospital dependent on the erratic generosity of the general public for its existence.

After its staff and patients had departed for the new premises on Grosvenor Street, the Frederick Street hospital was rented for a period to the Board of Guardians. It was then adapted for use as an hotel. It was finally demolished in 1936. No trace of it remains. Like the nurses' home across the road, its former site is now a car park, an anonymous place that shows no sign of the dramas and tragedies that were the lot of the people that lived and worked, suffered or died there in the nineteenth century.

3 A Fresh Start 1903 – 1922

The official opening of the new Royal Victoria Hospital was a far cry from the precipitate and unceremonious opening of its predecessor in 1817. Instead of a hasty occupation in the middle of a fever epidemic, the opening ceremony on 27 July 1903 was performed by the new King, Edward VII, with all the accompanying pomp of a Royal occasion. A touch of pathos was added by the lovely Queen Alexandra, who dedicated Ward 17 in memory of her eldest son the Duke of Clarence.

Nor did the new red-brick buildings bear much resemblance to the Frederick Street Hospital. In order to accommodate the revolutionary new Plenum system of ventilation, the seventeen, sixteen-bed wards were built in a single storey on one side of a long corridor.[1] Beds for eye, ear, nose and throat patients, the Extern Department and the Dispensary lay on the other side. Rising above them were East and West Wings which provided residential accommodation for nursing, domestic and medical staff – the latter carefully segregated in East Wing. The strict demarcation that existed between the dwellers in the two Wings is commemorated in a rhyme popular in the hospital in the early years of the century:

> East is East and West is West
> And never the twain shall meet
> Unless in the way of duty,
> Did the D.O.B.* repeat.
> But there is neither East nor West,
> Nor duty, nor D.O.B.
> At night in the kitchens when pupils
> Are drinking their cup of tea.

* According to preference translated as 'Dear Old Bostock or 'Damned Old Bitch'.

Later, as the number of nurses increased, extra rooms were found for them in the two small single-storey buildings initially used as septic and isolation wards, until the upper floors of the new King Edward VII Memorial Building (KEB) became available in 1915. In 1919 further rooms were provided in huts erected in the grounds.

The main corridor, which linked the various parts of the new building, was for many years a focal point in the life of the hospital. In the course of the day virtually everyone had occasion to walk at least part of its length, and it became a recognised meeting place for working colleagues and friends. There a junior nurse, working in a ward with a difficult sister (and every generation has had at least one of these) could receive sympathy from a friend; and many a romance blossomed in corridor meetings, accidental or contrived. It was also, however, a place where Matron might be encountered, casting a critical eye in passing on the uniforms of her nurses in case they were anything less than immaculate, or halting a running nurse in her tracks with a stern, 'And where is the fire nurse?' – fire and haemorrhage being the only acceptable reasons for running in the hospital.

The transfer from the old to the new hospital took place on 17 September 1903. While lacking the pomp of the official opening, it was, nevertheless, a complicated operation; but so well was it organised that it took just two hours to move some seventy to eighty patients, none of whom apparently suffered any ill effects. The hospital's own ambulance (horse drawn) was supplemented by others from the Fire Service, the Union workhouse and the Royal Irish Constabulary, and by a fleet of omnibuses and cabs. Some specially trained policemen were also on hand to help. Last to leave was the Matron, Miss Bostock; accompanying her in the cab were the Cook, Kate a wardsmaid and the Dispenser, Mr Cole.

Mr Cole, a fine and competent dispenser, was unsparing in his efforts on the hospital's behalf. Fiercely opposed to waste, in later years he became something of an ogre to nurses. He looked with distinct displeasure on those who came through his doors bearing broken syringes for replacement; and his rather forbidding expression was, at times, the final straw for junior nurses sent by Sister to the Dispensary for medicines or pills with incomprehensible names. One such nurse, having been told to fetch, urgently, some *caffeine benzoate* for a collapsed patient, on arrival in the Dispensary dissolved into tears, mumbling, 'Sister sent me for something … it *sounded* like "coffee hen"'. With his vast experience, Mr Cole was able to translate, and sent her hurrying back to Sister with the correct drug.

The strangeness of medical terminology to the raw, nervous,

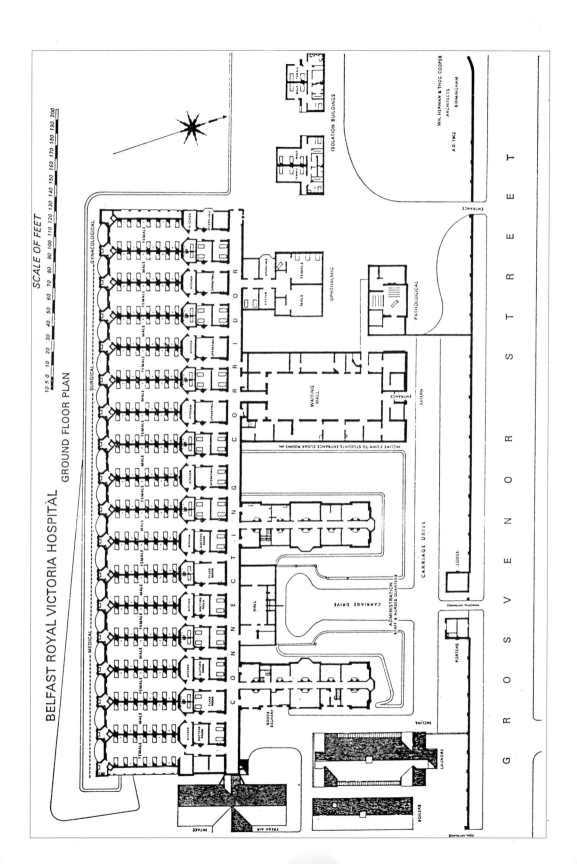

BELFAST ROYAL VICTORIA HOSPITAL
GROUND FLOOR PLAN

SCALE OF FEET

10 5 0 10 20 30 40 50 60 70 80 90 100 110 120 130 140 150 160 170 180 190 200

Wm. HENMAN & THOS. COOPER
ARCHITECTS
BIRMINGHAM

A.D. 1902

G R O S V E N O R   S T R E E T

inexperienced nurse has been a recurring problem over the years. One relative newcomer, dutifully reporting a telephone message to the ward sister, informed her that there was a pile of letters for the ward. Sister, slightly puzzled by the message, was enlightened a few minutes later when a patient arrived for admission – suffering from pyelitis! There was, however, a sense of achievement for the probationer when terms such as 'Omnopon and scopolamine' or 'thrombophlebitis' first rolled easily off her tongue; and no self-respecting junior of several months standing would dream of referring to a fractured femur as a broken leg.[2]

In addition to medical terminology, the new nurse – often from rural Ulster – had to learn the local idiom of patients, many of whom came from the neighbouring Falls and Grosvenor Roads, the interpreters often being fellow patients. One nurse, puzzled by the blank expression on the face of a new patient who had just been asked if his bowels had moved, was advised by the patient in the next bed, 'Ask him if he's been to the yard, nurse'.

Because there was not enough money available at first to staff and maintain the whole hospital, four of the wards (7,8,15 and 16) were not opened until 1914 when they were needed for wounded servicemen, Wards 7, 8 and 15 being used for patients and Ward 16 as an X-ray dark room. The Government paid the hospital for each casualty, which helped to cover the extra expense. Later Ward 2 and the Isolation and Septic Wards were also used for servicemen. When the war ended in 1918, although money was still short, all the wards were kept open.

Between November 1914 and April 1919, 1209 soldiers and sailors, and 100 armed services pensioners were treated in the hospital, with only nine deaths – three soldiers and six sailors, most of the latter from pneumonia developed as a result of having been some time in the sea after their ships had been torpedoed. At first the casualties arrived within a few days of injury, having been shipped to Dublin from France or England, and then sent by rail to various parts of the country. Later, many of the wounded sent to the Royal were convalescents, which did not please the consultants,[3] who believed that their skills were most valuable in the acute stages of injury or illness. As a result, a request from the military authorities for more beds in the Royal was turned down.

In recognition of the work of the nursing staff in caring for the war casualties, the Matron, Miss Bostock, was awarded the Royal Red Cross, First Class in 1916 and three years later was given a war bonus of £100.

Opposite: A revolutionary design. Plan of the new single storey hospital in 1903, with its 'community' corridor and row of Nightingale wards. (RVH, Belfast)

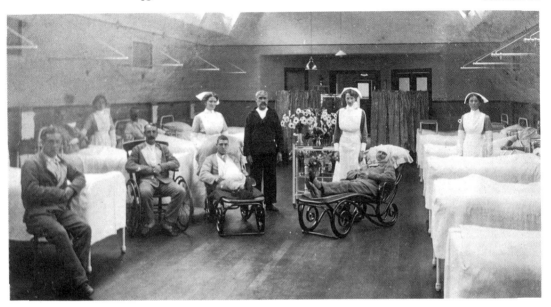

*Out of the Front Line.
First World War
wounded in ward 15
in the care of Sister
Elizabeth Elliott.*
(Mrs J. Kirk,
Dundonald)

By the time the war started in 1914 Miss Bostock was well established as Matron. The task that faced her when she first took up duty in
1903 was a formidable one, but she was well equipped for it. Mary
Frances Bostock trained in the Leeds General Infirmary from 1880-
1883, where she remained as a staff nurse for a further two years. A
year as Superintendent of the General Hospital, Barbados, was followed by a further two years as Night Superintendent in the Monsall
Fever Hospital. She was appointed to the Throne Hospital as Lady
Superintendent in 1887 where several members of the Visiting Medical
Staff had the opportunity to assess her capabilities and recommend
her appointment to the Royal Victoria Hospital.

A trim, slender-waisted woman of forty-two on her appointment,
Miss Bostock became rather more rotund over the years, and in her
long grey dress, white apron, and cap with its under chin bow, she
was a familiar and rather awesome figure as she went about her daily
duties. One of her probationers likened her progress to that of a ship
in full sail. She was well-respected as Matron by both nursing and
medical staff. One consultant said of her, 'She had the attributes of
Royalty, and was treated as such'.[4] Although generally a strict disciplinarian, she said it was her duty to see that rules were carried out, not to
make them, and was human enough to turn a blind eye to minor
infringements. A bunch of keys deliberately rattled as she walked
through the corridor door to the ward was sufficient to alert the clandestine tea-drinkers in the kitchen, giving them enough time to pop

their cups into the ready-open drawer, close it, and draw the back of a hand across their mouths to remove all traces of this forbidden activity, before stepping forward to meet Matron and accompany her on her ward round, or to busy themselves elsewhere.

The first Royal nurse/ matron. Miss M.F. Bostock in Frederick Street before the opening of the new hospital. A well-liked and respected lady, she was Matron from 1901–22. She chose to wear the symbolic nurses' apron.
(RVH, Belfast)

Although hospital matrons are not renowned for having – or at least showing – a sense of humour, Miss Bostock certainly had one. Young Sister Montague, when escorting Matron and a sick nurse to be seen by a rather unpopular and irascible ear, nose and throat surgeon, in her anxiety moved his chair a little too far back, with the result that he sat down hard, and inelegantly, on the floor. Although no physical damage was done, the surgeon was far from pleased and Sister, apprehensively escorting Miss Bostock and her charge from the examination room, fully expected a severe reprimand for her carelessness. She was amazed instead to see her dignified Matron, once out of earshot of the offended Consultant, dissolve into peals of laughter – and loved her for it!

The post of Matron, combining as it did the work of both Lady Superintendent of Nurses and Housekeeper, carried many responsibilities. She supervised the nursing service, to which she appointed all staff; she could suspend but not dismiss nurses. She was also reponsible for the training of probationers, and in the absence of the Medical Superintendent took charge of the hospital. As mistress of the household her duties included supervision of the domestic work of the hospital, the catering, the supplies and the laundry. In each of these spheres she had to ensure that the greatest economy was exercised. Indeed, her skill as Matron was judged as much on how economically she could provide these services as on the quality of the service provided. She had to keep the relevant records and deliver a written monthly report to the Nursing Committee, a sub-committee of the Board to which she was responsible, and which alone had the authority to dismiss nurses. All of this Miss Bostock did for an annual salary of £100 which, by the time she retired in 1922 had risen to £250.

Although she had no secretary to help with the considerable volume of paper work which fell to her lot, Miss Bostock had helpers. An assistant matron/home sister was appointed to deputize for her in her absence, and to take charge of the nurses' home in West Wing. The first to hold this post was a Miss Davis. She resigned in 1905 and was succeeded by Sister Mugglestone, then Miss Hilson, who remained until she was appointed Matron of the Throne Hospital in 1909. Miss Hilson's successor was Miss Manser – known to the nurses as The Green Hen because she wore a green uniform dress. She was rather more concerned with the letter of the law than Miss Bostock was, and in an endeavour to make the nurses conform to the regulation that the wings of their Sister Dora caps be pinned close to the head, carried a supply of pins for the purpose. The nurses, who thought that the wide wings were more becoming, refused to conform for long, and released the newly-pinned caps as soon as Miss Manser was out of sight. When Miss Manser resigned in 1919 she was succeeded as Assistant Matron by Miss A.E.Musson, and a separate post of Home Sister was created, the first holder being Sister Niblock, a Glasgow-trained nurse who had been a ward sister in the hospital since 1905.

The Sister Dora caps (which were made up by the night nurses from starched semicircles of linen) were only one of the changes in the nurses' uniform in the new hospital. The most noticeable change was in the colour of the dresses, scarlet for sisters and Royal blue for the nurses. The nurses' short stiff cuff was replaced by a white oversleeve.

When removed for work in the ward this could be folded and tucked into the bib of the nurse's apron, ready to put on again if she had to venture out on to the main corridor. Rolled up or uncuffed sleeves were *not* allowed to be seen there. Black shoes with rubber heels to reduce noise, and black stockings, barely visible under skirts which had to be no more than three to four inches from the ground, completed the outfit.

Architect's impression of the front (left) and rear (right) of the new hospital. In the front view Queen Victoria overlooks the main entrance. The rear view shows the balcony ends of the wards. In both, East and West wings tower above the other buildings.
(RVH, Belfast)

Although it was common practice at the time for matrons to undertake all housekeeping duties, because the Royal was a large hospital the Board decided to appoint a housekeeper to help Miss Bostock. She took care of the day to day management of the kitchens and looked after the resident doctors and pupils in East Wing, but was responsible to Matron who remained in overall charge. It must have been either a particularly difficult or unpopular post, initially at least, as there was a rapid turnover of housekeepers for a number of years. Most appear to have been nurses with housekeeping certificates (obtained after six months in a hospital kitchen) and they possibly found the work beyond such a limited experience. Later, housekeepers were specifically trained for this work, two of the most outstanding and long-serving being Miss Inglis and Miss Crothers.

In addition to the Assistant Matron and the Housekeeper, the third main helper for Matron was the Night Sister. There is no record of who the first one was; Miss Bostock herself supervised the night nurses until she was appointed. Miss Manser held the post from 1908 to 1909 when she was succeeded by Sister Catherine Dynes, who had completed her training in the hospital the previous year, and who was destined to become one of the most famous personalities to walk the Royal corridor – never to be forgotten by those whose paths crossed hers. 'Diana' as she came to be known, reigned over the Royal at night for forty-four unbroken years.

One of the all-time greats. Sister Dynes in benevolent mood. The only traceable photograph of her, obtained by subterfuge when she was awarded the MBE in 1953.
(A&C Photography, Belfast)

A devout Roman Catholic, she fasted from midnight and faithfully attended Mass each morning on coming off duty. She never broke this strict fast, no matter how busy or arduous the night was. She was afraid of no-one in the pursuit of what she saw as her duty. Pupils, housemen, and even consultants bowed to her authority, and to her wisdom. Woe betide the raw houseman who failed to expedite surgery if Sister Dynes, in her highly distinctive drawl, asked, 'What are you waiting for? – his abdomen's as hard as a board. He must have perforated.'; or who sent home a drunk with head injuries against her advice. The night nurses – ephemeral though they were, as each nurse in turn did her periodic spell of night duty – were hers, and she strongly resented interference in their affairs, even from Matron herself. She not only knew and recognised regular patients – often to their discomfiture, if the claimed illness was not entirely genuine – but assessed with remarkable accuracy the diagnostic ability of general practitioners whose patients were sent for admission, acknowledging the competent with a nod of approval, and the incompetent with a derisive 'Hmph!' Never afraid of hard work, and, under an apparently stern exterior, sensitive to the feelings of the young nurse in the half unreal, rather eerie, world of the hospital at night, she seemed to know by instinct where she was most needed. On many occasions she sent probationers to other duties, rolled up her sleeves and set about some particularly unpleasant task for which the nursing staff was responsible. Laying out a patient after a death in the ward was never a popular task; to have to do the same for a badly mutilated accident or suicide victim in the lonely and echoing confines of Extern in the small hours of the morning was infinitely worse. It was here, perhaps, more than anywhere else that Sister Dynes' sensitivity was most apparent.[5]

She was strict but she was also very fair. A nurse on her first night duty was closely watched until Diana was satisfied she would do her work properly. If she felt she had misjudged anyone and chastised them unfairly, she did not apologise directly, but let them know by her attitude that she was aware of her mistake.

Although stern in appearance, Sister Dynes had a most winsome smile, particularly when she was amused – an emotion she was not always successful in concealing. A good-humoured running battle of wits continued between herself and successive generations of pupils, whose pranks she secretly enjoyed, even if, as befitted her office, she officially had to frown on them. She was even known to complain if their behaviour was too good!

Over the years she evolved her own version of the Royal uniform. She retained the red dress, square-bibbed apron, black shoes and stockings worn by ward sisters when she was promoted in 1909, and also the oversleeve of her probationer days. She did, however, shorten her skirts in accordance with current fashion, and adopted the Army sisters' cap when it was introduced in the 1920s. Her impact on all who passed through the hospital was profound, from patient to senior consultant. For decades, wherever Royal friends met throughout the world, anecdotes of encounters with Diana would be (and still are) exchanged with affection. It was a measure of her enduring influence, that, some twenty-five years after she retired, my husband – himself an ex-pupil and houseman of the Royal – came home one day from the hospital to report, in shocked tones, 'I met a *consultant* to-day who had never heard of Diana!'

Apart from Sister Dynes, for a number of years most of the sisters in the Royal had been trained outside Ulster, and indeed Mr T.S.Kirk, one of the consultant surgeons, insisted on having an Englishwoman as his ward sister. Of the eight appointed to the hospital by the end of 1905, only three had trained locally. However, as more Royal-trained nurses became available, Miss Bostock seems to have given them preference when vacancies occurred.

In many ways the work of the ward sister was akin to that of Matron but on a smaller scale. She, also, was responsible for the nursing of the patients, but only those in her own two-ward unit. She, also, was expected to teach the probationers, but only those who worked in her wards. She had no say, however, as to which nurses should come to her wards or when they should go; this was entirely in the hands of Matron and her Assistant. The ward sister also had a housekeeping function in her own unit where she supervised its cleaning – by nurses and wardsmaid, ordered and served the patients' meals, and saw to it that ward supplies were maintained and that its stock of linen and equipment was kept in good repair. Once a year she had to give account of her stewardship an annual stocktaking, when every piece of linen and every item of equipment had to be laid out for checking, ward number clearly visible.

For most ward sisters this ritual, performed by Matron and the Assistant Matron, was a nightmare, as authority frowned heavily on those who could not produce on the day the requisite number of sheets, pillowcases, pyjamas, theatre socks, spoons or knives, clearly marked with the ward number. Borrowing, although often unavoidable, was also disapproved of. For some sisters the answer was to hide some of the objects most likely to stray – pyjamas, socks and teaspoons being particularly susceptible – producing them for stocktaking only. One innocent nurse on stocktaking morning was delighted to see a heap of fluffy new theatre socks in a ward noted for their scarcity. Her joy was short-lived, as the socks, once counted, were promptly returned to Sister's locked cupboard!

A wary watch from the corridor door on stocktaking morning, to find out in which direction Matron was heading as she left West Wing, gave forewarning of who was to do the count in that particular ward. Groans were heard if the 'spy' reported, 'We've got Matron!', sighs of relief if she was seen to move off in the opposite direction.

Because all cutlery was especially vulnerable to theft, and because teaspoons in particular seemed to be incurably attracted to the scrap bucket, every knife, fork and spoon had to be checked each evening by the junior probationer on duty and a diligent search of all possible hiding places (including the scrap bucket) made for missing items. Some sisters refused to accept that it might *not* be the fault of the nurse doing the check if a piece of cutlery was missing, which resulted in one desperate probationer on night duty (when cutlery also had to be accounted for) telephoning her mother to ask her to go at once and buy a teaspoon like those used in the hospital, have it engraved with the ward number and bring it to her so that she could make up the full number and get off duty!

Although responsible to Matron for all her work the ward sister was directly answerable to the medical staff for the care of the patients. She had to see that the doctors' instructions were carried out, be they inexperienced houseman or senior consultant. The wise houseman – usually advised by his predecessors – made an ally, not an enemy of Sister. Because ward sisters normally remained in post for some years

*A theatre visit.
Medical and nursing
staff pose in ward
theatre (c. 1910).
When operations were
in progress only the
sister and junior
probationer would
have remained.*
(RVH, Belfast)

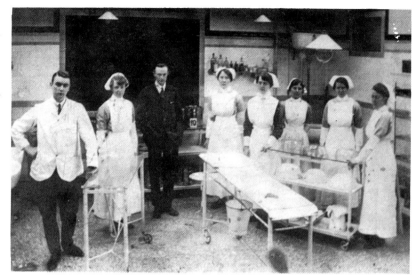

they were able to learn the likes and dislikes of the consultants for
whom they worked and thus the best way to keep them content. As
these men were often temperamental and difficult, it was a foolish
new house physician who did not heed Sister's advice in these matters
but went blithely on his way ordering *pil dig. folio* which, though
pharmaceutically correct, was *not* the favoured drug of Dr Marshall
(who preferred his cardiac patients to be treated with *Digoxin*) but of
his arch-rival, the Consultant in the adjoining ward. Similarly, an unwary house surgeon in the gynaecology wards could rue the day he
did not listen when Sister told him that Mr Greer preferred his patients
to be prepared for operation with the lotion known as 'green paint'
and not iodine – the usual method. Mr Greer's reaction to a patient
arriving on the operating table in front of him 'prepped' with iodine
was not an experience to be repeated!

Care of the theatre, its equipment and its preparation for operations
was an extra chore for the surgical ward sisters. Although they were
present in the theatre when the surgeon was at work, their role was as
'stage manager'. They 'handed' instruments for the surgeon but did
not assist with actual operations. The more menial work in the theatre
was done by a probationer, and while many enjoyed the novelty,
others found its remoteness from the conscious patient unappealing.
There was much work to do, brasses to be cleaned, scalpels to be
taken to the cutler for sharpening, dressings prepared and, on operating days, instruments and gloves to be boiled. Miss Montague, as a
near-centenarian, recalled polishing the brass on the table in Wards 11

and 12 theatre so energetically that a part fell off and, to her great embarrassment, had to be sent to England for repair. Her crime seemed even worse because this particular table was reputed to be the one on which King Edward VII had had his appendix removed.

Each surgeon's eccentricities had to be learned. One nurse in 1911, mindful of the teaching she had been given about the maintenance of aseptic conditions in the theatre, was surprised to see the eminent surgeon, Mr John Walton Brown, start to operate dressed, not in the customary white gown and mask, but in a stained morning suit. (He kept his better suit for doing the ward round!) She was even more surprised in the middle of the operation to see him put his rubber-gloved hand into his pocket for his spectacles and, having placed them on his nose, continue with the operation without further ado.

Nurses themselves could err in their efforts to maintain sterility. Some twenty years after the episode with Mr Brown, a nurse preparing a dressing tray dropped a pair of sterile forceps on the floor, and carefully retrieved them using Cheatle forceps (forceps used, almost as an extension of the nurse's arm, for handling sterile instruments and dressings). Only when the original forceps had been retrieved did the absurdity of her action dawn on her!

Big Maggie at work. Margaret Cranston, for over thirty years wardsmaid in Wards 11 and 12, where she was both the bane of the nurses' existence and an essential helpmeet. (Mrs R.M. McDonald, Bangor)

The supervision of the wardsmaid's work was a part of the ward sisters' duties that had to be exercised with great diplomacy, as a veteran wardsmaid could be as temperamental as the most senior consultant. These women had great loyalty to their wards and often outserved several sisters. Their proprietorial attitude to 'their' ward, and invaluable contributions in fields strictly outside their official duties, is delightfully illustrated in the story told of Big Maggie, for many years wardsmaid in Wards 11 and 12, who one day greeted a staff nurse from another ward with, 'We havn't time to attend 'til you – me an' Tony (the Houseman) are puttin' up a gantry'.

Lizzie Turner, wardsmaid in Wards 9 and 10 was another memorable personality. Lizzie, who insisted that she was the illegitimate daughter of a noble lord (unidentified), refused to let the nurses make tea for 'her' patients because she did not think they could do it properly.

The junior nurse who did not keep on good terms with the wardsmaid could be in as much difficulty as the houseman out of favour with the ward sister. Strong-minded probationers who, at first, scorned the idea of ingratiating themselves with the wardsmaid in order to enlist her help, soon found that they could not always manage without it. On a busy afternoon, when her services were often in demand elsewhere, she found that it was almost impossible to prepare and distribute the patients' afternoon tea if the wardsmaid did not help, particularly if there were no patients able or willing to help by pushing the trolley.

Much of the junior probationers' work in the ward was still domestic – dusting, cleaning brasses, washing the white paintwork, cleaning the baths and toilets. Although she no longer had to scrub floors, she did have to sweep them each evening when the wardsmaid had gone off duty. She had also to scrub the ward and kitchen tables every day, taking great care in case any water should splash onto the polished wooden floor and incense the wardsmaid who had spent long hours with a heavy polisher, or 'bumper', maintaining its shine. She had to ensure that the lid of the bin, which had to be carried out to the main corridor first thing each morning, was thoroughly polished. With so much polishing to do, and polish often scarce, many probationers carried their own tin in their pocket, as having no polish was not accepted as an excuse for work not well done. It was also the junior's job to wash all the urinals, bedpans and other enamel ware daily. The two-way tap provided in the toilets for this purpose could provide the unwary with an unexpected and most unwelcome showerbath. Various methods were devised to clean the urinals, shredded newspaper in water being one. A more drastic method tried at one time, sulphuric acid, was undoubtedly effective, but had very painful consequences when not thoroughly rinsed away! The most unpopular of all her cleaning duties was undoubtedly the daily emptying and washing of the sputum mugs.

In between the domestic chores, the junior distributed food and bed-pans, fed helpless patients, inspected new female patients' hair for vermin, and applied a strong-smelling sassafras compress covered by an embarrassingly conspicuous towel turban if she found any – the only kind of treatment the junior nurse was entrusted with.

Her duties often took her out of the ward (which could be a welcome escape from a particularly difficult or irritable staff nurse or sister). She carried soiled linen to the Laundry – having first sluiced it in the ward, and soiled dressings to the incinerator in the yard. She brought broken crockery weekly to Matron for replacement, collected the drug order from the Dispensary, and the daily order of stimulants (stim) from the main kitchen.

As even-more-lowly newcomers arrived to slot into the bottom rung of the ladder, the junior probationer became a senior probationer – unless there was an unusual excess of staff, when she became an extra, helping wherever she was needed. As senior, her work was more in keeping with what she had imagined nursing to be. She

blanket-bathed the bed-bound, tepid-sponged the feverish and cos-
setted pneumonia patients in home-made jackets fashioned (by the
nurses) out of gamgee – a cotton-wool wadding sandwiched between
gauze. In the surgical wards she also prepared patients for operation.
She had not yet, however, escaped the domestic round. The ward
dusting had to be done, including a twice-weekly high dusting with a
long-handled brush and she was expected to fill any spare minutes
scraping bed wheels clean of fluff, or turning out and cleaning patients' lockers.

Because economy demanded the maximum use of probationer
labour, relatively few qualified staff nurses were employed, and most
nurses left the hospital after training. It was common, therefore, for
third-year probationers to have to undertake work which was properly the province of a staff nurse. Many of these duties involved giving
the patients their prescribed treatments – applying poultices, giving
inhalations, doing surgical dressings. She was also responsible for
maintaining the stock of drugs and lotions and for giving the patients
their daily medicines. She even occasionally gave injections, although
this was, strictly speaking, the houseman's duty. As an acting staff
nurse she would also deputize for the ward sister.

The departure of a number of sisters and staff nurses to the armed
forces during the First World War left the hospital short of trained staff
as the Board had agreed to hold enlisting sisters' posts, and replace-
ments were not employed for them when they were called up.[6] Staff
nurses were replaced. There were not always enough, however, to
ensure that there was a trained nurse for each ward unit. At one point,
in 1917, it appeared that only probationers would be available to take
charge of some wards if the remaining sisters were allowed to take
their annual leave.[7] (The records do not reveal if the sisters got their
holidays.)

Neither ward sisters nor staff nurses had to do night duty, but
nurses in training had to do three months each year. It says much for
the Night Sister that she was able to run a large hospital at night
without trained staff.

Although all meals were provided for the day staff in the West
Wing, the night nurses, had to make their own midnight supper. A variety of dishes were produced, some imaginative, others barely edible.
In one ward kitchen the nurses might sit down to a light soufflé
omelette, while next door the menu could be a greasy fry, or toasted
slab cake, left over from the patients' tea. It was strictly forbidden for
housemen or pupils to eat supper with the night nurses, a rule more
frequently recognised in its breach than its observance. Successive

The Belfast District Lunatic Asylum, razed to the ground in 1923. The site is now occupied by the Royal Maternity Hospital, Musgrave and Clark House and Mussion House.
(RVH, Belfast)

generations of doctors, pupils and nurses became adept at concealing the evidence of guests at the first sound of the Night Sister's approach, the quietness of this late hour being a distinct asset as Sister Dynes did not follow Miss Bostock's practice of rattling keys.

Night duty in hospital was, and still is, a strange twilight world. Some nurses found it extremely difficult to adjust to sleeping during the day. The night nurses' rooms were on the top floor of West Wing, but although this was quieter than the lower floors, the everyday noises of the hospital could still be heard. For others it was a decidedly scary time, especially in the remoteness of Extern or the Septic and Isolation Wards, or even when sitting alone in the small hours in a darkened ward of sleeping patients. Until its inmates were transferred to Purdysburn in 1917, the possibility that a dangerous lunatic might have escaped from the neighbouring Asylum sent shivers of fear through night nurses when prowlers were seen in the grounds near the wards. The phenomenon of night nurses' paralysis would occasionally strike a half-asleep nurse who, seeing, or imagining she saw, the Night Sister standing beside her chair, found herself totally unable to get to her feet, a heinous crime given the strict hospital etiquette of the age.

Night duty was a time when nurses got to know their patients in a way not always possible under the eagle eye of Sister in the rush and bustle of day duty. Many firm friendships were also established between nurses of different seniority as they shared the night watches together. In marked contrast was the misery of a junior who found herself partnered with a lazy or bad-tempered senior (the second or third year nurse in charge). The consequences of such an unfortunate partnership were worst in the busy early morning when the night nurse single-handedly had to prepare her patients for the day ahead – serving breakfast, washing, distributing bedpans and bedmaking. At times, when the ward had more than the usual number of helpless patients to be washed, and perhaps no able-bodied helpers among the rest, the task was almost impossible if started at the official hour of six o'clock, and it often became necessary to risk the Night Sister's wrath – if caught – by doing some of the work before the lights were put on, a hazardous procedure in semi-darkness, with both ears and one eye on the door!

A way of monitoring the whereabouts of the Night Sister was vital if unofficial activities such as early washings, or entertaining housemen to supper, were to remain undetected. Telephone calls from ward to ward, notifying her progress, were one method – most nurses being blissfully unaware that Sister Dynes could both hear and understand the sound of the telephone bells which preceded her along the corridor, clearly audible in the quiet night! It was also possible, by careful inward adjustment of the swinging corridor doors, for a nurse on her hands and knees to watch for the approach of the Night Sister while herself remaining virtually invisible. It was a system, however, which depended on an unchanged routine and if Sister Dynes chose to approach from the opposite end of the corridor to that from which she was expected, the first the nurse knew of her approach was when a familiar voice enquired dryly, 'Were you looking for me nurse?'

When the Royal moved to its new premises in 1903, a number of partially-trained probationers came too. Whenever extra nurses were needed, more probationers were brought in, usually singly but occasionally in twos or threes. They had to be between twenty-three and thirty years of age – although one, by wearing her mother's clothes to Matron's interview, managed to get in at eighteen.[8] If the preliminary requirements of good health and character references, and an adequate standard of education had been met, the final selection was made by Matron at an interview. The standards on which she based this selection are not recorded, but her written comments on nurses in training give some indication of the qualities she approved of in her staff. A 'conscientious', 'hardworking' nurse merited unquestioning

*Forbidden guests:
night nurses' supper
1950s. The
houseman and pupil
guests (the empty seat
being the
photographer's) are
strategically placed
for quick retreat if the
Night Sister should
arrive unexpectedly.*
(Mrs I. Mcdonagh,
Coleraine)

approval, but was there an element of doubt about the selection of a
nurse who turned out to be 'flighty'?

There was usually no problem in getting probationers for the new
modern hospital, in spite of the fact that both other general hospitals,
the Mater Infirmorum and the Union Infirmary, and some of the
smaller specialist hospitals were also offering nurse training. The fact
that, by the early twentieth century it was already acceptable for the
middle-class girl, as well as her working-class counterpart, to undertake paid employment, swelled the pool of potential candidates. While
many of the growing number of clerical and secretarial posts in Belfast
were filled by city girls, nursing attracted more from the rural areas.
Over the years some 75 per cent of nurses training in the Royal have
come from outside the city.

The attraction can hardly have been the money. For the privilege of
working in the hospital, probationers, (who paid a premium of £20 on
entry) received no pay for the first year, £10 for the second and £12 for
the third. In 1918, during a period of difficult recruitment, a small
payment was introduced for first year nurses. They did, however, have
free board, lodging, uniform and laundry. Nevertheless, most probationers, for the first year at least, were dependent on help from home
to pay for necessities such as shoes and stockings, which were not
provided.

The free board and lodging was probably an attraction for country girls seeking work in the city. The belief that the nurses' homes were strictly supervised almost certainly influenced their parents in deciding whether or not to allow their daughters leave home for the bright lights of the city. And strictly supervised they were. Matron and her assistants took their *in loco parentis* responsibilities very seriously. Nurses had to check out when leaving the home, and were required to check in again no later than 9 p.m. Numbered brass tags, one for each nurse, which were housed on a board in the Home Office, were collected by the nurses on their way out and replaced on their return. A glance at the board enabled the Home or Night Sister to see who was in or out. A nurse who forgot to hang up her tag when she returned was liable to be brought from her bed to do so. Lights had to be out by 10.30 p.m. and a tour of the bedroom corridors about this time by the Night Sister ensured that the rule was obeyed. However, lights were unnecessary for clandestine visits to friends' bedrooms. On these occasions, if the night round had not already been done, a careful listening watch was kept for Sister Dynes' soft-footed approach, when a breathholding silence could prevent detection. Late theatre passes were allowed once a month, but shortage of ready money meant that this privilege was not often sought; and, anyway, as Matron disapproved of too frequent requests it was wiser not to incur her displeasure – and perhaps be labelled as 'flighty'! Social contact with the medical staff, except at carefully chaperoned dances, was forbidden. Nurses were not allowed to play tennis with either doctors or students; and nurses suspected of being 'frivolous' were kept well away from privileged areas such as Extern, where supervision could not be so strict. This is not to say that there was *no* social contact. There were always means of getting round any rule, and more than one marriage resulted from friendships made in the hospital.

While the strict discipline was sometimes resented by the nurses, much of it was intended to ensure that they had adequate rest, for the work of the probationer was still physically very hard. With no preliminary instruction to soften the impact, and often no other newcomer starting with her with whom she could confide and share her problems, new probationers, on their first day, were sent to work full time on the wards. The day staff was called at 5.45 a.m. for breakfast at 6.30 a.m., by which time a nurse was expected to have made her bed, tidied and dusted her room, ready for inspection by the Home Sister. She had to be ready to start bed-making in the wards at, or before, 7 a.m. and finished work when the night nurses came on duty at 8.30 p.m.

In addition to a monthly day off, nurses had a half day, either morning or evening, on Sunday; one evening each week from 4.30p.m.; and two hours off each other day, either from 2 p.m to 4 p.m. or 5 p.m. to 7 p.m.. Night nurses had one night off a month. Although their working week was sixty-six hours, this was not excessive for the time and indeed was less than nurses worked some other hospitals. In the neighbouring District Lunatic Asylum the Management in 1911 was 'pleased to be able to reduce the working hours of the nursing staff to seventy a week'; and in Guy's Hospital, London, in 1908, nurses were working an eighty-five hour week.[9] In 1919, in order to reduce the working week for Royal nurses to fifty-six hours, an eight-hour shift system was introduced, but at the nurses' own request this was swapped for a weekly day off. Each nurse also had three weeks annual leave; Matron and the Assistant Matron had thirty days.

For the first few months at least, weary and footsore probationers wanted to do little else in their off duty hours but bathe their feet and lie down. As they became accustomed to the work, they did more with their leisure. They swam in the Falls Baths, and played tennis and croquet in the hospital grounds where, on a sunny day, it was sometimes pleasure enough just to sit and chat with friends. The dances given by the Board or the doctors were popular, and occasionally they took tea and buns with former patients in the streets nearby.

Food was very important to these hard-working girls. The hospital meals were good, and the food plentiful but unexciting, so any nurse who lived in the city or who was able to afford the fare to a more distant home was expected to bring back 'eats' to share with her friends.

Probationer in Sister Dora cap. Uniform had to be immaculate, with skirts no more than four inches from the ground. Miss Bostock introduced the Sister Dora caps for all staff (sisters retained their bows) and oversleeves for staff nurses and probationers, and later for herself.

Amid the routine came occasions of high drama. As a result of the Celtic Park riots in 1912, which followed Winston Churchill's anti-Home Rule speech, the hospital was inundated with casualties and anxious relatives. One nurse, relishing the drama and excitement of the occasion promised herself, 'If this is war, I'll be in the next one' – and she was.[10]

There was other rioting uncomfortably near to home. The disturbances which occurred on the Falls and Springfield Roads in 1907 during the dock strike, following the 1916 Rebellion, and before and after Partition in 1921, were unpleasant experiences for the nurses. Gunfire kept them awake and frightened at night, and night nurses returning to their rooms in the King Edward Building sometimes had to pick their way through broken glass, a legacy of the night's activities.

Because economic necessity had made the probationer the mainstay of the nursing service of the hospital, it was almost inevitable that her training suffered as a consequence. Priority was given to staffing

Changing hemlines and footwear

1890 – 1920

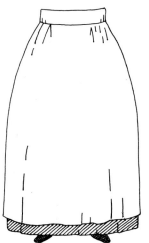

long dress and apron
black shoes and stockings

1920s

shorter dress
white shoes & stockings

WW2

strapless apron
no stockings!

1946
under Miss Elliott

Fashionable A-line dress
Stockings (plain) restored

(1950s - apron straps restored)

1960s
under Miss Robb

Mini-skirt era!
white shoes and
stockings (popular)

1980s

Skirts longer again
White shoes and
stockings retained.

Joan o'neill

the wards, not to ensuring that every probationer had as wide a range of experience as possible. It was common practice, both then and for many years after, for a probationer to be sent back more than once to the more specialised wards such as Gynaecology or Ophthalmics, where she had already gained some experience and was therefore more useful, even though a period in some other department might have been personally more beneficial. However, the wide range of diseases dealt with in both medical and surgical wards in the years before specialization became common, ensured that the majority of probationers got fairly wide experience. Most spent at least a short period in the theatre and in 'Gynae'.

For practical instruction in the nursing care of patients, the probationer was dependent on the ability, inclination and spare time of the sister under whom she was working and, perhaps more importantly, on the nurses senior to her in the ward.

The theoretical content of nurse training came from two main sources. Matron and the Assistant Matron taught nursing, until Sister Niblock was appointed as Home Sister, when she took over Miss Bostock's teaching duties – but not her overall responsibility for training. Consultant surgeons and physicians gave regular lectures, the principal subjects being anatomy, physiology, surgery, medicine, gynaecology and ophthalmology. The Housekeeper gave lessons in invalid cookery. Lectures were held in off-duty time and any night nurses taking them had to rise from bed to attend. Examinations were held at the end of each course of lectures, and a certificate awarded on successful completion of three years training. In the absence of a classroom, lectures were held in the Board Room or Linen Room, whenever sufficient probationers of the appropriate grade had accumulated.

The general purpose textbook used was J. K. Watson's *A Handbook of Nursing*. First issued in 1899, it was regularly revised as new areas of work developed. More recently trained nurses might be surprised to discover that Watson emphasised the importance of treating, 'not merely diseases but human beings', who were to be dealt with 'tactfully, without favouritism, gently and quietly and made feel at home'. The thinking behind the modern concept of holistic treatment is not just as new as we have been led to believe.

Changing hemlines.
After having risen
steadily for a century,
then settled, the RVH
hemline is again on
the move, but this
time downward.

When they finished their training, most nurses left the hospital. Many of them married and left the profession, which by this time had become one almost exclusively for single women. Of the remainder, some went into private nursing, others became district nurses, and a few remained in hospital service. A number of the latter in turn be-

came matrons of other Ulster and Irish hospitals; Miss A.P Knox in the
Royal Belfast Hospital for Sick Children, Miss Elizabeth Elliott in the
Belfast Ophthalmic Hospital, Miss Neely in the Benn Hospital, and
Miss S.K.Stewart in the Adelaide Hospital in Dublin, and later in
Musgrave Park Hospital, Belfast, were four who trained in the Royal
under Miss Bostock. Some chose to join the nursing services of the
armed forces. There, particularly during the war, they had an opportunity for travel rarely possible then for any but the well-to-do – and
nurses were certainly not in that category!

While mostly occupied with her work in the hospital, Miss Bostock
was also Vice-president of the Ulster Branch of the International Nursing Association and concerned with the general development of nursing in the Province. An enthusiastic member of the College of Nursing
from its formation in 1916, she became a founder member of the
Belfast Branch in 1921. As a strong supporter of state registration for
nurses she was appointed to the General Nursing Council for Ireland
(formed to implement the 1919 Nurses' Registration Act), and served
on the Joint Nursing and Midwives Council when it replaced the
General Council in Northern Ireland. For a time after her retirement
she acted as its Registrar.

While she was Matron, the number of beds in the Royal rose from
196 to 350 and the total nursing staff from about 44 (Matron, 6 sisters, 2
staff nurses, 34 probationers) to 132 (Matron, Assistant Matron, Home
Sister, Night Sister, 11 sisters, 8 trained staff nurses, 17 acting staff
nurses, 92 probationers) including two nurse-masseuses (the first full-
time appointment to this post having been in 1907), two Sisters in the
Electrical Department, and one for electrocardiographic work.

Miss Bostock retired in 1922 and the Board gave her a pension of
£150 a year. She died in 1950 at the age of ninety.

In spite of the disruptions caused by international and civil wars,
and the ever-present need for economy, the first two decades in the
life of the new hospital must have been viewed in retrospect with
some satisfaction by all concerned. The unified nursing management,
with Matron responsible for both service and training, ended the
conflict which had marred the latter years in Frederick Street. For the
nurses, the new buildings, with relatively few stairs, were a vast
improvement on the old hospital, although its air-conditioning system
could be enervating. These were, however, the days before antibiot-
ics, and for many patients, particularly those suffering from pneumonia, good nursing was still the only hope of recovery. They were also
the days before insulin, and many nurses found it distressing to have
to stand by helplessly as a diabetic patient lapsed into inevitable coma

and death, or to see epileptics denied surgery because it was considered inadvisable to give them anaesthetics. In spite of this, and the
long hours, small pay and hard work, most of the nurses who later
recalled those years insisted that they had been – for the most part –
happy ones.

4 The Doors Open Wider 1922 – 1939

Although the First World War had ended in 1918 there had been little peace in Ireland, north or south, in the following years. But by the summer of 1922 the Government of the new state of Northern Ireland had established some sort of control in the Province, and life began to return to near normality. Nothing however would be quite the same again.

The immediate impact of the First World War on the Royal had been the temporary loss of staff to the armed services, and the admission of war casualties; but its influence continued into the post-war years. Attitudes were changing. The camaraderie of war had blurred the clearcut class distinction of the Victorian and Edwardian eras, and the close working relationship that doctors and nurses had enjoyed in the services was filtering through into civilian life. Although nurses were still far from being regarded as equals, the medical staff was becoming a little less authoritarian and a little more paternalistic. The gaiety of the flapper era even penetrated the cloistered precincts of the nurses' homes, albeit in a very dilute form. Discipline became a *little* less strict, and even mixing of the sexes was officially condoned.

One of the few positive contributions that war has made to society over the centuries has been to speed up advances in medical science. Not surprisingly, it has been in the field of surgical treatment that most advances have been made, and in the First World War the effect of these advances was enhanced by improvements in anaesthetics and by the administration of intravenous fluids – blood in particular. In contrast, developments in medical – as opposed to surgical – treatment were few, with two notable exceptions. Insulin was first used in the Royal to control diabetes in 1925, and injectable liver extract not only gave new hope to victims of pernicious anaemia but it improved their quality of life as they no longer had to face a daily ration of chopped raw liver.

It was wartime experience of military and naval hospitals that began to change the attitude of the middle classes towards the institutional treatment of injury and disease. Previously, hospitals had been regarded primarily as refuges for the sick poor. But now, while minor surgery was still carried out in private houses (tonsils were often removed on scrubbed kitchen tables), full use of many of the advances in treatment could only be made in hospitals, or the new nursing homes that sprang up in the 1920s. Treatment in these homes, however, was expensive. It was beyond the means of the less affluent in the middle classes, and it was they who led the new demand for hospital beds.

The demand for beds and the growth in scope of hospital treatment convinced the Board of the need for further expansion, even though money was still short. Fortunately the new Government of Northern Ireland, through the Ministries of Home Affairs and Labour,[1] was prepared to help with grants; and appeals to the public, including one through the new medium of wireless in 1935, and another in anticipation of the coronation of King Edward VIII, helped to maintain a flow of contributions. These ranged from huge legacies like the £130,000 left by Henry Musgrave to the penny-a-week schemes organised by the RVH Working-men's Committee. (Few nurses were aware of how much the Committee did for the hospital, and at times let themselves be irritated by the occasional member who, rather self-importantly, insisted that he had a right to enter the wards at any time, including the sacrosanct periods of medical staff and bedpan rounds.)

The first step towards expanding the hospital was taken in 1923, when three more wards were added and the corridor extended to accommodate them. These were longer than the existing wards (a total of twenty-five beds in each – including the sidewards). Each new unit had a modern operating theatre, and a new theatre was also added to the Ophthalmic Wards.

Away from the main corridor, the Dental Department was transferred from Extern to the top floor of the King Edward Building, displacing the nurses who had rooms there. They were housed temporarily in the recently completed wards until the new Musgrave Wing of the nurses' home, which linked the East and West Wings, was ready in 1925.

The ex-army hut vacated by the dentists was adapted for use as an

Miss Musson and her senior staff in their new army caps. Each matron refashioned the uniform according to her own taste and the style of the times. The front row includes, from the right, Sister Elizabeth Elliott, Sister Alice Steele, Miss Montague, Miss Musson, Miss Garvin (Sister Tutor), and Sister Brown, and, possibly, Sister Corkey. On the right in the second row is Sister 'Lizzie' Lynas. (The late Miss J. McAdam, Dundonald)

observation ward for Extern, where it became the only source in that department of a refreshing, though strictly unofficial cup of tea. In later years Observation was ruled over by Tilly the maid, who not only looked eccentric with her haystack of grey hair, short skirts and thick black stockings but behaved eccentrically as well. Those she favoured could do no wrong; those she disliked could do little right and were virtually ignored. One nurse got so exasperated with Tilly's intransigence that she dumped her, bottom first, into the bin – and then had some anxious moments getting her out again before Matron's round! Among the few possessions Tilly had with her when she died was the wedding photograph of one of her favourite nurses.

By the early 1930s the hospital's services were being regularly used by the whole Province, and the three extra wards were not nearly enough to meet the increased demand. The Board decided that the most economical way to provide more beds would be to lengthen the old wards to match the new; this would give an extra seven beds in each. The work was completed in 1937, increasing the number of beds to 538.

Unfortunately, the ancillary accommodation was not similarly extended, and one washhand basin and bath still had to serve twenty-five patients; however sluice-rooms were added, linking the balcony ends of the wards in each unit. Not only did these sluices make washing bedpans, 'bottles' (urinals) and sputum mugs easier,[2] but they provided a welcome refuge for nurses anxious to keep out of the way of Sister. By keeping an ear cocked for approaching footsteps down either ward, it was always possible to beat a hasty retreat into the other, or to emerge into the same ward innocently carrying a bedpan or bottle, complete with its red cover, or other evidence of conscientious industry. Those who used the sluice as a place to have a forbidden cigarette were not always so successful at escaping detection, as the unmistakable smell of smoke was slow to disperse, even if the cigarette itself was out of sight.

Before work began on the first of the new longer wards in 1923, the hospital was given the option of buying the recently-vacated Asylum buildings.[3] The offer was refused as poor sanitation made them unsuitable for development, and the whole magnificent structure unfortunately had to be demolished. Some of its stones were used in building the new wards, and its bricks in the construction of a new boundary wall. The rest of the site was sold to the Queen Street Children's Hospital and what is now the Royal Belfast Hospital for Sick Children (RBHSC) was built in a corner of the grounds. Three new buildings later occupied the ground where the Asylum had formerly stood. The first, in 1933, was the new (Royal) Maternity Hospital (RMH), transferred from its old home in Townsend Street. The second was a 280-bedroomed nurses' home which was was opened in 1937.

Its first Home Sister was 'Lizzie' Lynas, a rather forbidding lady, who had previously been Sister in Wards 11 and 12. Rules, she firmly believed, were made to be obeyed – without question or argument. One day she found it necessary to rebuke the assembled nurses in the dining room for the practice of switching dressing-table drawers from their rooms on the night nurses' corridor to their new rooms when going on or off night duty. As the transferred drawers did not always fit properly, the carpenter had often to be called in. Miss Lynas forebore to explain this, choosing instead to tell them sternly, 'Nurses are *not* to take down their drawers'. She was totally mystified by the explosion of laughter that followed.

The nurses were now adequately housed – for the time being at least. The next problem facing the Board was what to do about private patients, a question that had been troubling it since the war. While it was useful to have some patients paying towards the cost of their treatment – and it had always been the practice to admit a small number of private patients – the Board was very conscious that the original aim of the hospital had been to provide care for the sick poor; and with this in mind had appointed a lady almoner in 1930 to help the

Admissions Committee ensure that those who could afford treatment elsewhere would not occupy beds in the Royal or, if they did, that they would pay for the privilege.

One of the problems she had to deal with was the rising number of casualties from motor accidents. Most of these came from the middle classes and could afford to pay, but often left without doing so! Furthermore, the lack of compulsory motor insurance meant that the hospital could not always claim for their treatment. Finally, after much thought, it was decided to build a separate private patients' block (the third building on the old Asylum site) for those able to pay, but whose total income was no more than £600 a year – the wealthier, it was felt, could afford to use the nursing homes instead. Named the Musgrave Clinic in recognition of the bequest which had financed it, and with beds for fifty patients, it was opened in 1938.

A birthday party. Miss Musson launches the RVH Unit of the Student Nurses Association, 1927. It was the first in Northern Ireland. The goods on the stall in the background were sold to raise funds. (source unknown)

The next people in need of space were the pupils. Residence in hospital was not compulsory for medical students until 1938, and it had previously been possible to house the small number who chose to with the doctors in East Wing. Now they needed more rooms, so a hut was erected for them at the back of the wards. Invitations to attend the frequent parties held in the hut – forbidden territory for nurses – were accepted only by the 'bravest (or most foolhardy?) amongst them.

The hospital managed one further addition before the Second World War. A two-storey isolation block, Wards 21 and 22, replaced the original small Septics and Isolation buildings (popularly known as The Bungalows) in 1939 and was opened the following year. Occasionally, psychiatric patients were brought in here for treatment, who, unless carefully supervised, were liable to wander off into the grounds. Once again, unidentified figures in the grounds at night caused some apprehension, until a phone call to Wards 21 and 22 reassured the caller that no patient was missing. The well-known African athlete and medical student, Prince Adedoyen, innocently practising his hurdling in the grounds late one evening, caused a temporary panic amongst passing nurses who mistook him for an escaped psychiatric patient!

To outward appearance, all this growth suggested a comfortable bank balance. However, this was not so, and in all departments it was still necessary to exercise the strictest economy. Some consultants (all of whom gave their services free) were particularly zealous in this respect. Mr J.S. Loughridge, for one, was in the habit of cutting some of the swabs – carefully counted at the beginning of each operation – into two, creating problems for the nurse responsible for checking that all were accounted for before the patient could be sewn up. Dr Victor Fielden, an anaesthetist, was another who, in a determined effort to save electricity, switched off the lights immediately the operation list was finished, but before the theatre had been cleared up. As an economic measure it proved to be of doubtful value, as one day, in the ensuing semi-gloom, Dr Fielden slipped on a discarded swab and stumbled against a trolley loaded with jars of expensive catgut, all of which tumbled to the floor and were smashed. After that, lights were kept on until the theatre had been cleaned up.

Nurses too were expected to be economical. Half the cost of breakages attributable to carelessness rather than accident had to be paid; and while one broken thermometer was tolerated – the misdemeanour having to be reported personally to Matron, who provided the replacement – subsequent breakages had to be paid for at one shilling a time.

In 1922, as well as a new state and a new government, there was a new matron, Miss Annie E. Musson. An Englishwoman like her predecessor, she had trained in the Nottingham General Hospital where she had been a ward sister and Night Superintendent. She had further experience as as a theatre sister in the Throat Hospital in Golders Green, London; as a sister in the King Edward VII Hospital in Cardiff; and as Assistant Matron of the Royal Gwent Hospital in Newport. On the outbreak of war in 1914 she went to France with the Territorial Army Nursing Service, where part of her service was in casualty clearing stations. (Few nurses were allowed so near the battlefront.) In

recognition of her work she was made an Associate of the Royal Red Cross and mentioned in dispatches. It was in France that she encountered Mr Andrew Fullerton, a member of the RVH staff, who was there as a consultant surgeon to the British Army. Greatly impressed by what he saw of her, he persuaded her to come to the hospital after the war, where she was appointed Assistant Matron, in place of Miss Manser. Others were obviously equally impressed with her ability, as she was invited to take over the post of Matron when Miss Bostock retired.

Although apparently a rather aloof woman – one nurse recalls being spoken to by her only twice in four years – she was considered an excellent matron, both by the medical staff and by her senior nursing colleagues, who found her to be very understanding, fair and progressive. Her office inevitably set her apart from the more junior nurses, for, to the probationer, Matron, however good or understanding (and had not every matron been a probationer once?) was an awesome figure, to be avoided if at all possible. Some of these nurses, who came to know Miss Musson better in her retirement, were amazed to find her cheerful, friendly and outgoing. The fate of matrons is to be misunderstood.

She in turn was succeeded as Assistant Matron by Miss S.K. Stewart, a tall blonde lady known to the nurses as Miss Frost (whether the nickname originated from the colour of her hair or her temperament is not known!) Significantly, she was first Royal-trained nurse to hold the post.

Sister Niblock, who had been appointed Home Sister in 1919 when Miss Musson arrived from France, remained in this post for twelve years. A dour Glasgow-trained Scot, she was a martinet who enforced a strict and unsympathetic discipline in the Nurses' Home. Unlike other members of the senior nursing staff she made no concession to the more relaxed atmosphere of the post-war years. She refused to let even the tiredest nurses use the lift – it was, 'Not for the likes of us'. That is not to say that it was not used when her back was turned! Like Sister Dynes she developed her own variation of the hospital uniform. When Miss Musson introduced the army sisters' cap , Nibby chose to retain the frilled cap and bow she had first worn as a ward sister under Miss Bostock; and although she adopted the navy dress chosen by Miss Musson for assistant matrons and home sisters, she insisted on wearing a white apron on top. What most intrigued members of the hospital staff, however, were her elastic-sided boots. These could be seen peeping from below her long skirts, or neatly set outside her bedroom door in West Wing – where a mischievous nurse popped banana skins into them! One day, on a routine round of inspection in East Wing, Miss Musson found a picture of Nibby's feet, complete with boots, hanging on a wall in the doctors' quarters. She removed it and, very much amused, told her Assistant Matron, but tactfully refrained from revealing her discovery to the owner of the boots.

Ill-health forced Nibby to retire in 1931, after twenty-six years service. At that time, although Miss Bostock had been given one, there was no pension scheme for Royal nurses. However after much consultation, the Board awarded Sister Niblock a single lump sum of £120. Her total income from savings at the time was £1 a week. With a weekly rent bill of 15s.0d. there was not much luxury ahead for Nibby in her declining years. ·

In 1935 a pension scheme was finally introduced, granting nurses 30s.0d a week on retirement. This innovation owed much to Miss Musson who had repeatedly pointed out to the Nursing Committee how difficult it was to get and keep good staff because of this lack of security.[4] It was not that the Board was unsympathetic, there is ample evidence to the contrary, but, as with Sister Niblock's pension, the question was whether it was legal to use money donated to the hospital for this purpose.

Another Royal nurse, Sister Alice Steele, (known in the 1920s as 'Alice Blue Gown' after the popular song of the day) succeeded Nibby as Home Sister. One of her duties was to see to nurses who reported

Nibby in unusually genial mood. Sister Niblock, a dour Scottish ward sister and Home Sister, rarely showed such an aimiable side to the nurses. (Miss F.E. Elliott, Melbourne)

sick. Rooms were set aside for them on the night nurses' floor where their only therapy was often a large dose of 'black jack' (a potent purgative). Nurses were not encouraged to report sick, and got little sympathy when they did, as their absence from the sparsely staffed wards could be ill-afforded. Sepsis, in the form of sore throats and infected fingers, was common, but otherwise they were relatively healthy – possibly because each nurse had to show a clean bill of health before she was accepted for training.

Miss Stewart resigned from her post as Assistant Matron in 1925, on her appointment as Matron of the Adelaide Hospital in Dubin. She was succeeded by another Royal nurse, Miss Anne Montague. 'Monty' was a quiet humorous woman, with a soft Dublin accent, extremely approachable and full of common sense advice for any who needed it, from Matron to the domestic staff. (One of the latter, Agnes McMaster, recalls Miss Montague persuading her to put a portion of her weekly wages into a Post Office Savings account.) In acknowledgement of her former Matron's wise ways, Monty also let her approach be known in advance by jingling keys or calling out before she came in sight. She retired in 1950 after forty-two years nursing in Belfast, almost all of them spent in the Royal. Like her contemporaries, Sisters Dynes and Steele, in her later years Monty was to see daughters and nieces of many of her early colleagues enter the hospital for training. She is remembered with great affection by hundreds of nurses, two of whom joined her, an alert and interested old lady, in Dorset in December 1985 for her hundredth birthday celebrations. She died in January 1986.

Whilst most of Miss Musson's appointments were Royal-trained nurses, some were not. One of the latter was Sister Isobel Brown, who arrived in 1923 – small, gentle, precise and lady-like. She introduced the Christmas carol-singing procession round the wards, with the pianist – Sister Calderwood – being towed along on the porter's trolley. It became a popular annual event, and although the length of the procession, with the tail still on the main corridor as the head wound its way round the darkened wards, made synchronisation of words and music rather difficult, it was enjoyed by staff and patients alike – the latter proudly identifying 'their' nurses and doctors among the throng.

Christmas in hospital was generally a happy time. As many patients as possible were discharged, and the wards were gaily decorated with paper streamers and lightshades, with careless disregard of the risk of fire – which fortunately never occurred. A potted palm was given as a prize to the most attractive ward, but as its leaves had to be dusted

'Do you take cream and sugar?' Sister Brown being 'Mother', dispensing tea in her treasured oriental china. (Mrs D. Neill, ex Belfast)

daily, the honour of winning it was not always fully appreciated.

For many of the staff Christmas Day started at 6 a.m. with Holy Communion in the Drew Memorial Church across the road from the hospital gates. Nurses were allowed to go in uniform so that they could be on duty for 7 a.m In marked contrast there was great frivolity on the corridor for the rest of the morning, mostly organised by the pupils, whose activities ranged from stealing kisses from any nurse they could catch (an activity not solely confined to students, even consultants were known to indulge!), to parading senior members of the Medical Staff, appropriately garlanded, on a trolley along the main corridor. In later years the students' pranks became much more boisterous; blanket-tossing and dousing in cold baths were just two of the Christmas 'presents' they gave to nurses who were unlucky enough to get caught.

The rigid demarcation of nursing duties was abandoned for the day, and with everyone giving a hand, the essential chores were soon

Time to relax. After the patients had been fed and attended to, Sister McCauley and her staff nurses entertain the medical staff and pupils to tea in the side-ward on Christmas Day 1947.
(Miss J. McCauley, Belfast)

done. Patients who were allowed up dressed in their everyday clothes, and the male bed-bound patients were wheeled round to the female ward where the tables were set for dinner. Sometimes ex-patients – usually ones who lived alone – were invited back to join in the festivities. With due ceremony the senior consultant carved the turkey and sliced the flaming plum pudding at the end of the ward, and the dinner was distributed by members of his family and the staff.

Dinner over, the wards were invaded by relatives and friends, the strict rule of two visitors to a bed being waived for the day. Meanwhile, the nursing staff, doctors and pupils retired to the sideward for tea. On Christmas evening a dance for the staff was held in the King Edward Building, and on the afternoon of Boxing Day the Workingmen's Committee put on a concert in Extern for walking and wheelchair patients (off duty staff often went as well) with items contributed by guest artistes and by artistically inclined doctors and nurses.

The next day, life returned to normal. Nursing routines (which had changed little since 1903) recommenced. Much of the work was still domestic: dusting, washing, polishing, and sweeping floors. The senior probationer in each ward still 'did backs' – preventing bedsores by rubbing the vulnerable areas with soap and water and methylated spirit, finishing with a dusting of talcum powder. It was not unknown for a tin of scouring powder to be mistaken for talcum, a mistake which the luckless patients were not slow to point out!

In the medical wards, pneumonia patients were still nursed through their crises in gamgee jackets (replaced in the late 1930s by flannel gowns), and patients suffering from kidney disease were sweated under wire cages fitted with multiple light bulbs in an attempt to rid their bodies of poisonous waste. Chronic chest disease was still very common, a consequence of poor housing and poverty. It was not unusual for nurses to meet the same individuals winter after winter, or even month after month, in different wards, as cold wet weather started them coughing and wheezing once more. The moist and even temperature of the Plenum air conditioning was particularly helpful for them, but provided what was all too often only a temporary respite. Many were very philosophical about their condition and, when readmitted for the umpteenth time, cheerfully greeted the familiar faces amongst the staff. Inhalations of Friar's Balsam and antiphlogistine poultices were often prescribed for them, but generally only as palliatives. The correct way to prepare an 'antiphlo' was to heat the tin of medicated kaolin in hot water, and then spread it on lint. The quick way was to make a cold poultice and then heat it on the side of a hot sterilizer, or under the grill in the kitchen. Attention dare not wander if the grill was used; blackened and charred poultices were not much use to anyone and, if it happened too often, the consequent need for extra tins of antiphlogistine had to be explained.

In spite of the presence of more middle-class patients (who, if male, were called by their surnames only), there were few refinements in what might be described as the hospital 'hotel service'. There were no trays for meals, and the ubiquitous thick delph mug was used in the male wards for tea, soup or porridge; women were given equally thick cups, but no saucers – only the semi-private side-ward patients had this luxury. Porridge was the most substantial item on the menu for the patients' last meal at 6 p.m, the alternatives being hot or cold milk, cocoa or Bovril – except for those fortunate enough to be on a diet which specified otherwise.

Other meals came from the main kitchen. From 1929, dinners were delivered in insulated, electrically heated trolleys, so there was less need to rush the food to the patients. The trolleys were usually plugged in at the centre of the ward where Sister or a staff nurse would serve the meals. Only Sister Benson (Benny) kept on serving dinners from the ward kitchen. She filled plates at high speed (a hangover from the days when speed was vital if the food was still to be hot when it reached the patients), with accompanying instructions to, 'Give that to the man with the head' or, 'Give that to the woman with the leg' to the total bewilderment of newcomers to her staff. (They soon discovered

'Give that to Mrs Smith, nurse.' Staff Nurse Gladys Deering deputises for sister at dinner time, 1947. (Dr P. Donaldson, Dundonald)

that the solution was to snatch the filled plate, urged on by Benny with a, 'Lift, nurse, LIFT – are you paralysed?' – rush with it into the wards, and then ask a longer-serving colleague who to give it to.)

There was more change in the surgical wards, where the advances in medical science enabled much more complex operations to be done, including chest and, occasionally, brain surgery. For some months, in an effort to reduce the lengthening list of men waiting to have hernias repaired,[5] Wards 9 and 10 were both used for admitting male patients for this operation, occasioning the popular rumour that the Consultant Surgeon, Mr H.P. Malcolm, a bachelor, would not operate on women! His name was cleared when the ward went back to normal.

The victims of the civil unrest that surrounded Partition were treated here too. Most were suffering from gunshot wounds, so the wartime experience of the ex-service surgeons was invaluable. Further Troubles in the early 1930s brought more admissions of the same kind.

The growing number of operations being performed made it impractical for the surgical ward sisters to continue combining ward and theatre duties, so staff nurses were appointed to all the main theatres. Only in Ophthalmics did Sister continue to take charge of the theatre as well as the wards. As more operations were also being done at night, an assistant night sister was appointed in 1925 to take over theatre duties from Sister Dynes.

The accelerating pace of life in the theatre made this work both more exciting and more worrying for the junior probationer. The unaccustomed close contact with the consultant surgeons was decidedly unnerving – strict hospital etiquette, which required messages to doctors to be channelled through Sister or the staff nurse, meant that junior nurses rarely, if ever, spoke to a consultant. All too often they found that their fingers became thumbs, and that their powers of rational thought seemed to become suspended when operations were in progress. One new junior, sent to change bowls of lotion, set a full bowl temporarily on a convenient stool – only to see the surgeon sit down in it before she could snatch it away or utter a word of warning. Some years later, another conscientious theatre junior, who was collecting used swabs for counting, found one trapped under the surgeon's heel. Enterprisingly – as she thought – she took out her scissors and snipped the protruding portion away, only to hear the surgeon roar, 'Who put the ****** light off?' His heel was also resting on a spotlight flex!

Mr Tom Smiley was one of the least terrifying of the surgeons, but junior nurses must nevertheless have breathed a sigh of relief when they heard him start to sing the Twenty-third Psalm – a sign that the operation was almost over, not an appeal to the Almighty for help! Ward staff on hearing it knew to expect Mr Smiley out for his coffee within a few minutes

It was not only in the theatre that some nurses found themselves suddenly bereft of reason. A junior nurse was told one day to clean the dentures of the male patients. Some fifteen minutes later her colleagues at work in the female ward, were startled to hear cries coming from the male ward. Thinking that some emergency had occurred, as many nurses as could left their duties and went to the rescue. What did they find? A group of nurses were gathered in the middle of the ward. Four were doubled over as if in agony, a fifth was standing sheepish and forlorn. In the middle of them all stood a basin filled with some sixteen rows of gleaming false teeth. What followed was chaos. In carrying out her instructions the nurse had collected all the false teeth together in one basin and meticulously cleaned each set. Not until she brought them all back into the ward did she realise that it was now impossible to tell who owned which teeth! Patients searched through the basin, trying to identify their own, some of them even argued over the same set of teeth. Everyone not directly involved was crippled with laughter.

While nowadays patients are mobilised as soon as possible after operation, in these years patients were kept totally bed-bound until their stitches were removed, which meant a lot more work for the nurses. A patient following a simple appendicectomy might lie for ten to twelve days; one who had had a hernia repaired lay for three weeks. The dangers of clotting, now associated with pressure or prolonged inertia, were not then fully understood. 'Donkeys' (a rolled

*Probationers in their
new VAD caps, having
an illicit smoke
behind the bushes,
1929.* (Mrs J.B. Young,
Drumbeg)

blanket put behind the patient's knees and tied to the bedhead) may have kept the patients from sliding down the bed – almost inevitable when a slippery long macintosh was sandwiched between the under-blanket and the bottom sheet – but they also increased the possibility of post-operative complications. Without them nurses had constantly to hoist patients up the bed to a more comfortable position. They soon learned the technique however, which enabled the slightest and small-est of them to lift the heaviest or most helpless patients with the minimum of discomfort all round.

The probationer remained dependent on help from the wardsmaid and patients. When none of her own were able to help, a night nurse might borrow a patient from the next ward to make the breakfast toast. Patients also dried theatre instruments, made dressings and sewed tapes on pillowcases (the Linen Room did other mending). While many of them welcomed the tasks as a means of passing the time, officially they were not supposed to be asked for help, so all sign of these activities had to be concealed during Matron's round.

This round was the rather dreaded high point of the nursing morn-ing – of much greater cause of apprehension than the twice-weekly Staff Day, when clinical teaching rounds were conducted by the Con-sultants. Much of the nurses' work in the first part of the morning was directed towards Matron's round. Dusting and cleaning were com-pleted before the 9 a.m. or 9.30 a.m. break, when nurses also changed into clean aprons.[6] As the hour of The Round approached, patients who were up were chivvied back to bed and every bed was carefully tidied, wheels straightened, corners aligned and bed-clothes pulled taut – pinioning the patient underneath. (After Matron had passed the bedclothes were loosened again.)

Her daily round covered the entire hospital. In the wards she was escorted by the senior member of nursing staff on duty. This was usually Sister or a staff nurse, but on rare occasions, if neither was available, to her horror, a more junior nurse had to deputize. It was a formal occasion, and uniform had to be correct. This meant that cuffs or oversleeves, which had been removed for work, had to be replaced before joining Matron.

Miss Musson managed to combine a rather formal, 'Good morning, how are you?' to each patient – usually answered by a polite, if inaccurate, 'Very well, thank you Matron' – with an eagle-eyed inspection of the nurses' work. Attention might be drawn (discreetly) to minute specks of blood on the wall, left by an inexperienced pupil in his quest for a sample of blood for laboratory testing, while a finger drawn along the footrail of the bed as she paused to speak to its occupant checked on the morning's dusting. On her passage through the ward kitchen Miss Musson would pause to peer down the spouts of feeding cups to ensure that they were spotless. In spite of her distant manner, she was not only aware of individual patients as she passed, but was very concerned for their well-being. One morning she noticed a young woman whose face was heavily disfigured by a birthmark. She returned to the ward later with her artist's palette and brushes and carefully camouflaged the blemish to show the girl what could be done with the aid of cosmetics.[7]

A second round in the evening, usually by the Assistant Matron or Home Sister, to get an up-to-date report on seriously ill patients, was less traumatic, as no inspection was involved. This report was then passed to the Night Sister.

Quiet was the order of the day for the Consultant's (or Staff) round, whether he was accompanied by a class of students or not. The demand for quiet was carried to extremes by some consultants who appeared to think that all patient care should be suspended while they proceeded slowly and regally on their way. One morning a dentist came to examine a patient in the ward while a particularly noise-conscious consultant was in the middle of his teaching round. The patient was rather deaf and the dentist had to raise his voice a little. Dr C****** stopped speaking, swept the students aside, went across to the intruder and said, 'I don't believe in two ministers preaching in the one church – you'd better go.' He went.

Nurses tiptoed about their duties in the ward while the round was in progress, and juniors washing bedpans in the sluice tried, usually

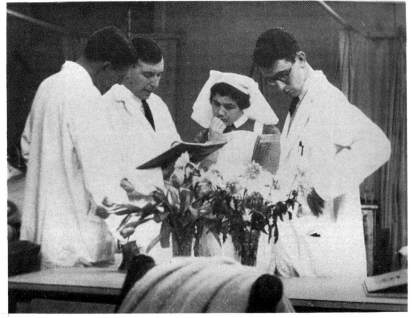

without success, to do so in silence. Those who had (or hoped to have!) friends amongst the attendant class of medical students reacted in one of two ways. If the task which brought them near the group was 'important' (such as taking a temperature or doing a dressing), no effort at concealment was made – rather the reverse. On the other hand, if it was necessary to pass the class carrying a bed-pan or, even worse, a sweeping brush and dustpan, avoiding action was taken with head bent to avoid recognition.

A new era merited a new uniform – or at least some change in the old one. Miss Musson, perhaps with a touch of nostalgia for her own army days, replaced the Sister Dora caps of her trained staff with the army sisters' fall (better known in the Royal as a big cap) and those of the probationers with the VAD cap.[8] She herself chose a blue woollen dress without an apron, but kept the traditional matrons' cap and bow. All skirts were gradually shortened in acknowledgement of current fashion.

At breakfast time on operating days, surgical ward sisters changed their black shoes and stockings for their theatre garb of tennis shoes and white stockings – raising the hopes of young Nurse Florence Elliott, (who was in a ward with one of the more unpopular sisters) that she was going off to play tennis! She was soon enlightened. From the late 1920s, all the sisters wore white shoes and stockings – at first only in the summer, when they were likened to the white summer hat covers worn by the tram drivers and conductors.

Nurses entering training had to provide their first uniform. On following years each nurse was issued with lengths of dress and apron material which she had made up as she needed it. (Many a toddler has had shorts or skirts made from uniform material left over from its mother's days in the Royal.) For many years Royal nurses had their uniform made up by F.E.Jeffries in Cromac Street. This semi-official status was acquired in the mid 1920s when a new probationer, as a gesture of thanks to Mr Jeffries, who had given gifts of linen to her church, asked him to make her first uniform. With gored skirts instead of the bulkier gathered skirts of other nurses, her uniform attracted the admiration of her fellows. They in turn patronised Mr Jeffries, and a tradition was born.[9]

In 1931 Miss Musson asked the Nursing Committee if a distinctive badge could be provided for nurses trained in the hospital. A small committee, including the artist and sculptor Rosamund Praegar, developed the familiar silver and green oval badge with its lamp motif, the first of which were issued in 1932. Originally made in silver, nurses were asked to pay 4s.6d. for it, but in 1947, when the cost had risen to 15s.0d., at Matron's request the Board abolished the charge for newly-qualified nurses.

For most probationers, the things uppermost in their minds were those to do with the minutiae of everyday life in the hospital. While they may have heard about the legislation of 1919 which introduced state registration for nurses,[10] few were probably aware of its immense significance. It was, without doubt, the single most important event in relation to the future professional development of nursing to occur in these years. Responsibility for the training curriculum and examinations was moved from the hospital Board to the Joint Nursing and Midwives Council for Northern Ireland (the Joint Council). The Registers were opened in December 1922, and nurses who had already been trained to an acceptable standard were invited to apply for admission. (RVH training was one of the first to be accepted by the Joint Council for registration at this stage.)

The next step was to invite hospitals to apply for recognition as training schools for the different Registers. The Royal, (along with the Mater Infirmorum and the Belfast Union Infirmary) was accepted at once – in spite of the fact neither it nor the Mater met one of the Joint Council's criteria for the General Register, that of providing experience in nursing sick children!

Hospitals which could not, or would not, meet these criteria could admit probationers as they had done before; but the training they offered could not be recognised for state registration. Some, however, applied for affiliated status, which allowed them to accept probationers for two years. If they were successful in the preliminary state examination (prelim) they could complete their training by spending a further two years in a recognised hospital. The Royal accepted a number of these nurses from Bangor Cottage Hospital and Enniskillen District Hospital, and from Ards District Hospital until it became a full training school itself.

Another group of nurses who came to train were those who had already qualified for one of the supplementary Registers – fever, sick children's or mental nursing. Having already passed prelim (which was the same for all sections of the Register) they could take their final for the General Register after two more years. After a short trial period as first year nurses they leapfrogged into second year.

A recognised training school had to employ a sister tutor. The first

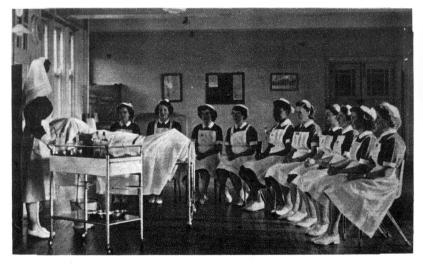

'And this is how you do it correctly.' Nurses in the demonstration room receiving instruction from Sister Tutor, 1950. Fifth from left is Nurse Iba Ituk, the Royal's first recruit from Nigeria. (Nursing Mirror, London)

one in the Royal was Miss Annie Moreland, who was appointed in 1923 at a salary of £150 a year. Although she had had some teaching experience, and proved to be an excellent teacher, she was not a qualified tutor. Nor were her successors, Miss Elizabth Garvin, Sister Tutor from 1926 until her death in 1935, or Miss Olive Daly, the first Royal nurse to hold the post, who returned to the hospital at Miss Musson's request in 1938. (A temporary tutor, Miss Hancock, took over during the interval). Qualified tutors were scarce, and it must have been a blow to the prestige of the largest voluntary hospital in Belfast to find that the Union Infirmary (the workhouse!) had been able to obtain one, where it had not.[11]

Although it had a full time tutor in 1923, it was 1925 before the school was given quarters of its own. When the new Musgrave Wing made the nurses' huts in the grounds redundant, Miss Musson had one fitted out as a classroom. This served until the New Nurses' Home was opened with a suite of rooms for the school, including a lecture theatre and a demonstration room. It was in the latter that new nurses learnt the rudiments of practical nursing, making beds, bandaging, setting trays, and performing various nursing procedures on a life-size dummy – an exercise which regularly sent their watching classmates into fits of giggles.

With the introduction of state registration, more attention was given to the actual process of training, although probationers were still admitted in ones and twos according to the needs of the hospital. Hard-pressed sisters often found the newcomers' total lack of experience difficult to cope with. One who arrived on Sister Elizabeth Elliott's ward on a Saturday morning, overheard a telephone conversation between Sister and Monty, who was appealing to her not to give the girl the following Monday as her day off. Sister was adamant. 'No I can't change it Miss Montague. It is one of my busiest days, and she is of *no* use to me, *no use at all.*' She was not to know then that the 'useless' nurse – Florence Elliott – would later become Matron!

In 1924 a simple form of preliminary training was started, a course being run at intervals when enough probationers had accumulated. Nurses taking the course started the day on the ward, spent from 9 o'clock until lunchtime in the classroom, then, after two hours off, went on duty again for the rest of the day. While this was an important step towards a then undreamed-of full student status for nurses, probationers still started work on the wards totally unprepared. Another fourteen years were to pass before this situation was rectified.

When the school had settled into its new quarters in the New Nurses' Home, Miss Musson asked the Nursing Committee for permission to establish a full preliminary training school (PTS) – the first in Northern Ireland. With her encouragement Miss Daly planned a course of lectures and visits to a pasteurisation plant, a bakery, and the Plenum ventilation system. Instead of the former ones and twos, probationers were brought into the PTS in batches of about ten every two months. At the end of the first month, they spent a few hours each evening in the wards. A third month of full time work on a ward gave the ward sister an opportunity to assess the probationer's work and attitude. If the report was satisfactory she was signed on. If not, she was given a chance to redeem herself with another sister before being refused a contract. The first full time PTS entered in December 1938. It meant a great deal more work for Miss Daly so a second sister tutor was appointed.

A year or two later, nurses taking final were given a few hours off duty for study – the birth of the study blocks of later years.[12] This indulgence was regarded as an imposition by some ward sisters, and Sister Brown refused to allow the finalist in her ward off until Miss Musson herself intervened.

This gradual introduction to hospital life was undoubtedly less traumatic for new probationers, younger now at eighteen and a half than their predecessors. The companionship of fellow probationers was also a great comfort. Even so the first evening on a ward was still something of an ordeal, with two rows of interested patients watching the newcomer's every move, fully aware of her lowly status, and ready to offer advice or shield her from the wrath of her seniors. However, neither form of preliminary training was sufficient to prepare the new nurse for every eventuality, as one junior, fresh from the classroom, found to her cost. Sent by Sister to, 'Clean the umbilicuses, nurse', she searched the ward diligently until she unearthed two umbrellas, which she duly cleaned with meticulous care! Sister's comments are not recorded.

There were other problems too. The up-to-date equipment in the school was often far superior to that found in the wards, and new probationers were perturbed to find that neither enough instruments, bowls nor linen were available to set trays in the way they had been taught. Instead of a well-laid out dressing tray she saw the staff nurse doing the dressings with a mere two bowls and one pair of forceps – using her fingers as a substitute for a second pair. The constant need for economy made improvisation the order of the day.

Once the honeymoon period of PTS was over, nurses had still to attend lectures in their off-duty hours. Many of them, because of a chronic lack of sleep and the unaccustomed pleasure of being able to sit down – nurses *never* sat on duty – were totally unable to prevent themselves catnapping through lectures. This had the dual effect of irritating the lecturer (one doctor was heard to mutter, ' ... casting pearls before swine ... ') and making coherent note-taking extremely difficult, if not impossible. Miss Musson, concerned about the time spent later by the Sister Tutor correcting their notes, tried, unsuccessfully, to get money for duplicated copies. Unfortunately there was none to spare.

The state examinations were held several times each year. Before being allowed to enter, a nurse had to pass prelim, complete the

They're here! Pandemonium at 9.45 a.m. in 'The Wing' as Final results arrive. (Miss M.E. Kerr, ex RVH)

required Joint Council programme of practical experience, and be given a good character reference by Matron. (It is not known if such a reference was ever refused.) If she passed, the probationer became a state registered nurse (SRN), and on the first Sunday after the results had been published donned her staff nurses' big cap.

Her first appearance in a 'big cap' was a momentous occasion for the newly-qualified nurse, who wore it with a mixture of pride, self-consciousness and just the suggestion of a stiff neck. Until she became accustomed to it, she was (happily) reminded of its presence each time she turned her head and, out of the corner of her eye, caught a fleeting glimpse of crisp white organdie.

In 1926, the Board awarded medals to successful finalists, and prizes to nurses in training. For the first few years these were presented at Board meetings but in 1930 Miss Musson combined a reunion of Royal-trained nurses with the prize-giving at an At Home. The gathering, which was entertained by a concert given by the nurses, was held each year until the war.

Dissatisfied because the examination results were not always as good as she would have liked, in 1937 Miss Musson tried to persuade the Nursing Committee to set an education standard of the Northern Ireland Ministry of Education's Senior Certificate for admission to training. While the Committee was sympathetic, and realised that sufficient candidates of this standard would probably be forthcoming, it was concerned that potentially good nurses might be rejected if a rigid rule was made. No immediate action was taken, however, as there was already a twelve month waiting list of candidates with Senior Certificate.

In selecting her probationers, Miss Musson was not only concerned about their standard of education but, like Miss Bostock, about their character and manners. A refined woman herself, she liked to see the same characteristic in her nurses, although she did not go as far as the matrons of some of the London voluntary hospitals, who invited applicants to afternoon tea in order to find out if their table manners were acceptable![13] 'Good tone in the ward', 'Good influence', were her highest accolades; 'Manner not cultured' or 'Ideals not high', suggested later dissatisfaction with her original selection.[14]

These standards of behaviour extended to off-duty activities as well. In 1938 some of the nurses' partners arrived rather drunk to the Christmas dance. Miss Musson was so angry that she cancelled all further dances, refusing to change her mind even when appealed to by some of the consultants. The annual staff dance was not resumed until after the Second World War. She may have even wondered if the relaxation of rules, which now permitted mixed tennis, had been premature.

The mixed tennis nevertheless was widely enjoyed. Not only were tournaments organised on the hospital courts, but joint teams of nurses and doctors played outside matches as well. With a whole day off each week from 1919, and 'curfew' extended to ten o'clock, there was more time for recreation. Irregular hours, and a reluctance to ask too often for specific times off duty, however, made it difficult to attend outside events on a regular basis, so most social activity took

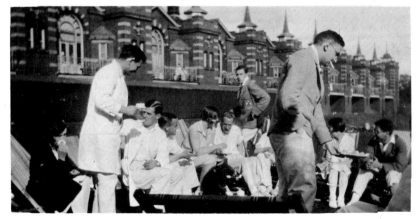

It's official! Doctors and nurses having tea during a tennis tournament c.1930, after Miss Musson had relaxed the ban on mixed tennis.
(The late Mrs M.E. Gilliland, Belfast)

place in or around the hospital. Badminton could now be played in the KEB hall – when it was not being used as a waiting room – and a hockey club was formed. Members made their own blue tunics and a pitch was provided near the New Nurses' Home. With some excellent players on the team, the nurses played against outside teams and a year later, in 1939, won a place in the Belfast League. For the more devout a nurses' missionary league was started in the early 1930s.

In 1927, an opportunity to become involved in the affairs of their

A bunch of enthusiasts. The Hockey Club 1937-38. Members of the club with Matron, and the hospital engineer, Mr Innes, who found them a ground to play on. (Mrs G.I. Fenton, Saintfield)

professional body, the College of Nursing, was provided when Miss Musson established a unit of the Student Nurses Association – the first in Northern Ireland.[15] But, although it enrolled sixty members in the first year (Miss Musson made it almost mandatory to join) it soon faded from lack of enthusiasm. Two years later it revived under the chairmanship of Nurse Aileen White, and began to thrive for the first time. As well as a busy programme of social events, it gave nurses the opportunity to meet their opposite numbers from other hospitals at different SNA events. An unexpected outcome of one of these visits was the startling discovery that Matron was human after all! The meeting was in London and Miss Musson had arranged for the Royal representatives to stay in the College's Cowdray Club, of which she was a member. Although staying in the Club herself at the time, Miss Musson tactfully kept well out of their way, but not before she had advised them to, 'Enjoy yourselves, and don't come in before the milk'!

As one of the two founders of the Belfast Branch of the College of Nursing and a leading member for many years (she was appointed Vice-chairman in 1928 – the first nurse to hold the office) Miss Musson was in an ambivalent position. As a College member she was dedicated to promoting the interests of the nursing profession, but as Matron of a voluntary hospital she was also conscious of the need for the utmost economy – and this inevitably included restricting spending on nurses.

With so much money being spent on buildings, there was little left for increasing nurses' salaries, which were often lower than those paid in workhouse infirmaries. There was some improvement however. In 1925, at Miss Musson's request, theatre staff nurses' pay was increased, and later other staff nurses with a second qualification were also given a rise.

Miss Musson's conscience about this extra expenditure seems to have troubled her, because in 1928 she suggested that it would save money if nurses who had completed their three year contract, but who had yet to sit their final, were paid as fourth year probationers –£35 a year instead of the current £55 – although in fact most were already acting as staff nurses. The suggestion, which followed the practice in some English hospitals, was adopted.

In 1934 the saving was increased by extending the training contract to four years. Nurses still became state registered after three years, but had to complete a fourth year before being given a hospital certificate which was essential in seeking further employment in nursing. In this fourth year they provided staff nurse service for fourth year probationer pay. Nurses already in training were strongly advised by Matron to 'take advantage' of this extra year and extend their contract – none was brave enough to refuse. (To her credit it must be said, however, that the experience gained in this post-SRN year was invaluable.) The hospital needed to have 20 – 25 trained staff nurses; under the new scheme two-thirds of the total would be the more economical fourth year probationers. Once again the need to save money was dictating terms of employment.

With limited openings for trained nurses in the hospital itself, those who did not marry when they finished training – marriage was still an almost total ban to further employment in nursing – had to seek work elsewhere; indeed Miss Musson preferred those who were appointed to the permanent staff to have had experience, if not further training, away from the Royal.

Extra qualifications were often needed, some of which could be obtained within the hospital. Six months' work in the kitchens entitled a nurse to a housekeeping certificate – useful for employment as a hospital matron. From 1938, when the Royal was recognised for training by the Society of Radiographers, one or two nurses at a time were seconded to the X-ray department to qualify in radiography.[16] In the 1920s Miss Musson tried to establish a school of massage (most masseuses at this time were also qualified nurses) but was unable to obtain a suitable teacher, and the project was shelved.[17]

Most secondary training, however, was undertaken elsewhere. Midwifery was popular, and essential for nurses hoping to get senior positions in hospitals with maternity departments. Edinburgh and Glasgow were favourite venues but from the mid 1930s an increasing number applied to train in the RMH, a choice encouraged by the award of scholarships to the three medal winners for 1933, and in the following year to an additional ten nurses with the highest examination marks.[18]

Further qualifications were not needed for all posts. To be an SRN was enough for those applying to the peacetime nursing services of the armed forces, the Colonial Service or to private nursing agencies or nursing homes. Of those who remained in the hospital services in Northern Ireland, a number later became matrons – one, Miss F.E.Elliott, returning to the Royal to succeed Miss Musson. Others went overseas to work as missionaries in Africa, India, South America and elsewhere. One black sheep remained at home to establish a brothel in the university area of Belfast!

When Annie Musson returned from France to become Assistant Matron and then Matron of the Royal Victoria Hospital, she must have realised that the years ahead would not be easy. Added to the many duties normally falling to the lot of the matron of a large voluntary hospital would be the work entailed in introducing state registration for nurses. But she almost certainly, having recently returned from 'the war to end all wars', would not have foreseen that, in twenty short years, she would be involved in leading nurses through a second world war – this time on the home front.

5 The Second World War 1939 – 1945

In the First World War the casualties treated in the Royal had been servicemen brought from France and the Atlantic to the safety of home. In the Second World War it was very different. The casualties were civilians, injured by the enemy in their own homes and workplaces on the very doorstep of the hospital. But in another way the pattern was the same as before. Many members of the past and present medical and nursing staffs enlisted in the armed forces as they had done in 1914, some of them never to return. Then, the war had been distant and horrific. Now, it was still horrific, but it was no longer distant.

The immediate concern was the need to protect the hospital against possible air raids, and prepare it for casualties should any occur. On September 3rd, within hours of the declaration of war, the glass in the ward windows was painted black, and orange bulbs substituted for white in all lights. Soon more permanent black-out arrangements were made, with black blinds attached to all windows, and shades, rather like cocoa tins, put on the lights, reducing their output to a glimmer. When no air raids occurred there was a gradual relaxation of tension. This inevitably led to some carelessness, and fines of 2s.6d. (12^1/2p) per offence were levied on nurses who allowed any chink of light to escape. A favourite practical joke at the time was to telephone a night nurse and tell her she was showing a light – sending the unfortunate victim on a wild goose chase, neck craned to examine each blind. This frivolous attitude was born of the belief that Northern Ireland was too remote from enemy-held territory to be in any danger of attack from the air – a belief also held by those responsible for its defence.

Because of it no other official air raid precautions were ordered, but, after a time, the Board decided on its own initiative to increase the hospital's defences. Brick shelters were built underneath the wards, with access by steps added to each balcony. Side ward ceilings and the windows above the three beds nearest the door were reinforced to protect patients who were too ill to take to the shelter. Fracture patients in traction were placed in these end beds so that they would not have to be moved in the event of a raid. The theatres without overhead windows (Wards 17 to 20 and Ophthalmics) also had their ceilings reinforced. A large static water tank was built in the grounds. This was sunk into the ground and doubled as a swimming pool for the staff – a popular venue in good weather. Buckets of sand and stirrup pumps were placed in each ward in case of an incendiary bomb attack; and hurricane lamps were provided for emergency lighting, as electric lights had to be extinguished when the air raid sirens sounded. The Whitla 'Good Samaritan' window was removed from the Extern hall for safe keeping. A fire warden was appointed and two hundred students enrolled as volunteer firewatchers. Two junior consultants slept in the Musgrave Clinic each night, in order to be on hand.

Two hundred beds were set aside for air-raid casualties, which reduced the number available for waiting list patients. Folding beds, provided later by the Ministry of Home Affairs, which could be erected down the centre of the ward in an emergency, enabled some of the reserved beds to be brought back into use. Repeated appeals to the Government to set up an emergency hospital were eventually answered in 1942, when room was found at Purdysburn Mental Hospital, from which most of the psychiatric patients had been evacuated. The Royal was allocated forty of these beds, and some waiting-list surgery was performed there.

From 1939, at the request of the Government, several hundred nursing auxiliaries were given basic training in the hospital. One of them, unused to the discipline of hospital life, unwittingly got a staff nurse in Wards 5 and 6 into bother. She arrived on Sister Brown's day off in time to share a plate of lemon toast – a favourite hospital delicacy, frowned upon as an extravagance by Sister Brown. The following day, the innocent auxiliary enquired if there was to be lemon toast with coffee again – Sister was *not* pleased, as the staff nurse found to her cost.

The unexpected finally happened in April 1941, when Germany launched the first of four air attacks on the almost totally unprotected city of Belfast. When the sirens sounded the juniors in the new nurses'

Some hospitals were less fortunate than the Royal. Examining the previous night's bomb damage at the Ulster Hospital, Templemore Avenue, 16 April 1941. (Belfast Telegraph)

home rose, dressed (by torchlight) in full uniform, and carrying a rug, torch, change of clothes, identity card and money (if any!) – all normally kept ready in a small suitcase – went to the basement shelter which was guarded by Sister Lynas. Having satisfied herself that each nurse's uniform was correct in every detail (and sending her back to her room to repair any omissions if it was not) she issued them with palliasses on which they tried to continue their broken night's sleep – bombs and gunfire permitting.

Senior staff went to their wards. On the night of one of the major raids, a nurse, obviously and understandably terrified, in an effort to bolster her failing courage began to sing to herself, a sound virtually inaudible amid the cacophony of the raid. It was audible however to Sister Brown, who greeted her arrival in the ward with a stern, 'Nurses do *not* sing on duty'. If Sisters Lynas and Brown were going to have anything to do with it, Royal nurses would face anything Hitler had to offer, dressed correctly and behaving with proper decorum.

Big Maggie, the wardsmaid of Wards 11 and 12, had her own ideas about the correct attire for these occasions. As she had not reported to the shelter by the time the bombs had begun to fall at the start of one raid, Miss Montague went in search of her. She found her struggling into her best – and rather stiff – corsets, determined that, if she was unlucky enough to be killed, she would not not be disgraced by being seen by the mortuary staff in her old corsets!

Once into the ward, where the only light was from hurricane lamps (a line of which also dimly illuminated the main corridor), the first task was to move the patients to the place of greatest safety. Patients who could walk were helped to the shelter, where mattresses and beds were in readiness; the rest were pushed in their beds to the sidewards, corridors or the reinforced ward ends. When all were settled and the vacated beds had been prepared for casualties, the staff nurse went to look after the patients in the shelter. Sister remained in the ward. In Extern, the staff stayed in the shelter under KEB until casualties arrived.

The first raid on the night of 7th/8th April, while inflicting serious industrial damage, caused relatively few casualties. The raid on the night of Easter Tuesday (15th/16th April) devastated the residential areas in the north of the city. An estimated 745 lives were lost and countless hundreds were injured.[1] Of these, the Royal admitted 120, treating a further 133 as outpatients. On the night of 4th/5th May, when the industrial areas were again hit and many homes in the east of the city destroyed or badly damaged, 96 were admitted and 94 treated as outpatients. While outside, the stricken, unprepared city was in chaos, with innumerable buildings wrecked and fires blazing unchecked because water mains had been shattered, inside the hospital, although a hive of furious activity (a normal night's intake was probably no more than half a dozen patients), the atmosphere was business-like and relatively calm.

Throughout the night of Easter Tuesday and the 4th/5th May, a succession of ambulances delivered up the dead and wounded. The former were identified (if possible) and sent on to the mortuary. The living were treated on the spot or admitted to the wards. Those with chest and less severe head injuries were sent to Wards 5 and 6. The severely shocked, but otherwise apparently uninjured, were put in Wards 7 and 8, which also had the sad responsibility of caring for those near death, for whom nothing more could be done. Any whose lives were at risk were operated on as soon as possible in one of the reinforced theatres. With lighting provided by Tilley lamps and the anaesthetics administered by dripping a highly inflammable mixture of chloroform and ether on an open mask, there were times during prolonged operations when those working in the theatres during the air raids felt they were in greater danger of injury from their own equipment than from the bombers overhead! The Royal was extremely fortunate in that, unlike the Ulster Hospital in Templemore Avenue which received a direct hit and was extensively damaged, it emerged from the air raids unscathed.

When the all clear finally sounded, patients were returned to their wards where many found that their beds had new occupants. However, places were soon found for the displaced, and drinks provided for those who wanted them. Only then were the exhausted day nurses free to return to bed, to try and snatch an hour's sleep before reporting for duty again at 7 a.m.

In the meantime lists of identified casualties were posted in Extern for anxious relatives to scan when the raid was over. For some nurses, the worst aspect of the air raids was not the bombs falling, or the casualties arriving, but the distress of the relatives the next morning, although the occasional happy reunions were some recompense.

In the wards the next day it was business as usual. Mr Greer, the gynaecologist in Wards 17 and 18, whose services had not been needed during the raid, insisted on doing his full scheduled operation list, even though his theatre staff had been at work throughout the night. Professor Crymble, whose surgical wards had admitted a number of the casualties, which had kept both medical and nursing staff at full stretch, complained because their notes had not been *fully* written up! It was, perhaps, their way of saying the show *will* go on.

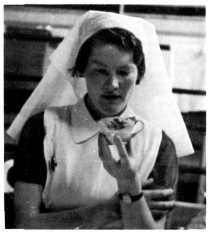

Was it the end of the war or her own future she was looking at? Sister M. A. McFarland, Theatre, Wards 11 and 12, reading the tea leaves sometime during the Second World War. In 1973 she became the first Principal Nursing Officer of the hospital. (Miss M.A. McFarland, Lisburn)

It was several days before surgery was completed on the less seriously injured. Those theatres which had been unusable during the air raids worked continuously throughout the following day and, in some cases, into the next day as well. Patients with multiple fragments of glass embedded about their persons were regular theatre visitors in the intervals between operating lists, when a few pieces would be removed each time.

For some of the nurses, their most vivid memory of these days and nights is of the exhaustion caused by lack of sleep rather than overwork. False alarms were frequent after the air raids. Two juniors, tired after a series of false alarm excursions to the basement, decided to remain in their rooms one night after the sirens sounded. They counted without Miss Lynas who, checking for absentees – there were always a few whom sirens, or even bombs and gunfire, failed to rouse – came to find out why they were missing. Expecting a severe scolding, they apprehensively feigned sleep. To their astonishment, the normally stern and unapproachable Home Sister roused them with a kindly, 'Wake up child! Don't you know the siren has gone?'

While the air raids were undoubtedly the war's dramatic highlight, a civilian tragedy, the early morning commuter train crash at Sydenham in January 1945, brought all the emergency resources of the hospital into use again. On this occasion too, the injured were admitted to any ward where beds could be found, the emergency take-in ward being quite unable to carry the whole load.

Apart from the catastrophic interlude of the air raids, life continued as normally as was possible within the limits of wartime constraints and shortages. Although the demand for beds was still growing, no new building could be done until the war was over. The urgent need for facilities for the growing specialty of orthopaedics was partly met in 1943 by converting a section of Extern into a fracture and orthopaedic clinic. The two sisters appointed to the clinic were sent to Manchester for specialised training, including the application of plaster of paris – formerly done only by the doctor. Although plaster bandages were available they were expensive so, for some years, they prepared their own – an unpopular chore as the powdered plaster was severe on the hands.

Food rationing applied to hospitals as well as to the general public, although patients were only required to surrender tea coupons. Nurses, whose ration books were deposited with the hospital, collected them when going on annual leave, but on days or evenings off had to depend on family or friends for meals. Small weekly portions of butter and sugar were issued to each nurse, who then had to decide whether to use all her butter in one delicious binge and do without for the rest of the week, or spread it thinly on her toast in the morning, or perhaps even eat her toast dry and keep her butter to disguise the taste of the thin gravy served with rabbit stew. Rabbit stew and rice pudding were the mainstay of the nurses' menu, although the cooks did their best to provide appetising and varied meals with the rations at their disposal. On one memorable occasion whale steaks were served, but the dark red meat with a fishy smell did not appeal somehow, and most of it was left untouched.

Economies in the use of uniform material were ordered by the Board of Trade, and so aprons were made without straps, and nurses' (but not sisters') sleeves were shortened, with an attached white cuff

We all have to sacrifice something. Wartime uniform with short sleeves, no stockings and no apron straps. (Dr P. Donaldson, Dundonald)

replacing the long half over-sleeve. Precious clothing coupons were required for stockings, so Miss Musson advised sisters and theatre staff nurses to save them by buying white stockings from the undertakers! When this source of supply finally dried up, a bleaching preparation called Strippit was used on coloured stockings, rendering them anything from cream to pale yellow – never white. From 1943 nurses were allowed to go stockingless – an unattractive, unhygienic and uncomfortable practice, with bare feet encased in black laced leather shoes. Assorted home-made concoctions of leg paint were used to try and disguise pale bare legs, with varying degrees of success.

As in the First World War, the loss of staff to the services created problems. Several consultant physicians and surgeons due for retirement remained at work, and others who had already retired returned to help. Because so many doctors enlisted immediately after qualifying, final year students were sometimes employed as housemen, while qualified housemen looked after two pairs of wards.

Within a year of the outbreak of war, not only had many of the permanent nursing staff joined up, but several fourth year nurses had broken their contracts and left to marry servicemen or to join the nursing services. According to the terms of their contracts they could have been refused a hospital certificate, but on further investigation it was discovered that to do so would be illegal. The question of discontinuing the four year contract was discussed but, as the hospital was having difficulty in keeping enough trained nurses, and as most fourth year nurses were either unaware of the loophole, or were unprepared to confront Matron with it, or, indeed, were quite happy to gain the year's experience, it was decided to let sleeping dogs lie. By 1945, when the number of staff nurses had shrunk from twenty-eight to eight, these fourth year nurses were carrying the major load of their work in the hospital. They were, of course, state registered, and in other circumstances fully entitled to staff nurses' posts. The shortage of qualified staff also meant that third and even second year probationers were frequently left in charge of wards for part of the day. Sisters' posts were kept filled, and for the first time a married, non-resident sister was appointed – to the Electrical and Venereal Diseases Department.

In 1941 the War Office appealed for more volunteers for the Queen Alexandra's Nursing Reserve. The pay offered was above that being paid to the staff nurses and sisters in the Royal so, in an attempt to prevent a wholesale exodus, Miss Musson requested, and was granted, an extra £5 a year for each trained nurse. She also refused to release some staff nurses on the grounds that they were doing essential war work.

As long as there were sufficient suitable applicants for training, the problem of staffing the hospital could be kept within bounds by increasing the number of probationers; but the number of applicants dropped during the war. In 1940 there were more than enough; a year later the number had halved. While Miss Musson had tried to keep the educational standard for entry at Senior Certificate level, this became increasingly difficult as many well qualified school leavers were attracted to the women's services. Pressure to accept a lower standard was also coming from some members of the medical staff, one of whom was particularly incensed when Miss Musson refused to accept two registered sick children's nurses from the Ulster Hospital (with which he was associated) for general training because she considered their education to be inadequate.

It eventually did become necessary to accept a lower educational standard and a formal entrance examination was devised for applicants without Senior Certificate. While its failure rate was high – sometimes 60 per cent or more – an increasing proportion of each intake was drawn from successful candidates, and a number of excellent nurses were recruited by this means. Miss Musson alone interviewed the applicants of Senior Certificate standard, but a member of the Board's Examination Committee joined her in the selection of the others.[2]

With so many school leavers entering the services, in 1944 it was decided to lower the age of entry yet again – this time to eighteen. There, however, Miss Musson insisted it must stop. Even if it meant that some seventeen-year-olds might slip through the net, because they would have to wait some months before starting training, she was adamant that no girl under eighteen should be asked to nurse male patients. The trial period was also extended from three to four months, to allow time for a second report on each probationer before a deciding on her suitability for training.

In spite of war and recruitment problems, the results in both state examinations in these years were extremely good. Miss Daly, who resigned in 1942, had proved to be an excellent teacher and is remembered by many for her ability to give new nurses an understanding of the pitfalls, duties and rewards of hospital life. She was succeeded as Principal Tutor by Miss Kate Huey, another Royal nurse and also an unqualified tutor. She was however, an experienced teacher, having taught both in the United Kingdom and in the United States.

There is, we are told, always a silver lining to the darkest cloud, and the dark cloud of World War Two showed a unexpectedly solid silver

It's over! Sister
Benson (right of
medicine cabinet), her
staff and patients
celebrate VE Day.
(source unknown)

lining in 1944, when substantial pay rises were awarded to the nurses on the recommendation of the Rushcliffe Committee. In an attempt to solve a nurse staffing crisis in English hospitals the Government had asked this Committee to look at pay and conditions and to recommend improvements.[3] Although there was no shortage in Northern Ireland, the realisation that the attraction of higher salaries in England might create one forced most hospitals to increase pay at once, and to introduce the recommended 96-hour fortnight and longer holidays as soon they could organise accommodation for the extra staff which would be needed.

The pay rise was made possible by a substantial government subsidy. Student nurses (the new name recommended by Rushcliffe for probationers, although they were still far from achieving real student status) were put on a scale of £40, £45 and £50 a year for their training years, rising to £60 in their fourth year before state registration and £70 after it. This was a very satisfying increase from the existing scale of £25 - £40. Staff nurses and sisters were put on a scale of £130 - £200 a year. The Rushcliffe Committee also recommended the abolition of a premium for training, – which in the Royal at this time was £10. Miss Musson, however felt that the already high drop out rate might increase if this was done, as the money was not refunded if a nurse left by choice. A compromise was reached in which new nurses would be asked for £5 (nominally to cover the cost of their board and tuition in preliminary training school – but in reality a ploy to circumvent the terms of the agreement) refundable to those who were eventually signed on.

Many Royal-trained nurses joined the armed forces, serving in all theatres of war. Regrettably, no full list of these nurses, or of those who served in the First World War, appears to exist. Of those known to have been on active service Miss Nora Earls, who left her post as Assistant Matron/Sister in the VD Department of the hospital to serve with distinction in North Africa and Palestine, was awarded the ARRC. She returned after the war. Others were less fortunate. Although the hospital and its staff emerged relatively unscathed from the traumas on the home front, some of those whose service took them overseas did not. Three ex-housemen, Doctors Robert Marshall, Humphrey Thompson and Norman Purce, all three of them sons of members of the Medical Staff, lost their lives.

At least five Royal nurses died overseas as a result of enemy action. Ruth Dickson (1913-1916) who had served with the Army in the First World War later became a missionary in Manchuria. Ordered to leave there in 1941 she was in Singapore working in a military hospital when it fell to the Japanese. She escaped on a ship which was then set on fire. She managed to reach an island only to be taken prisoner, and after three years of semi-starvation and overwork she died in Banka Island Concentration Camp on Christmas Eve, 1944. Ellen Lowry (1923-1927) and Ida Nelson (1925-1929) were in the Colonial Nursing Service stationed in Singapore. They were evacuated just before the city fell to the Japanese. Their ship was torpedoed and both drowned. Doreen Pedlow (1927-1929) was also in Singapore, serving with the Queen Alexandra's Imperial Military Nursing Service. She too was evacuated before the city fell, and was torpedoed. She survived to reach an island, from which she was rescued, only to have the rescue ship shelled and sunk. She drifted on a raft for three days and nights before she died. Beatrice Dowling (1937-1941) was serving in the Queen Alexandra's Imperial Naval Nursing Service and, like Doreen Pedlow, was rescued when her ship was torpedoed. As her leg had been broken she was sedated and put in a cabin until a doctor was available. Tragically, yet another torpedo found its target and she went down with the ship. The names of all five are inscribed in the Roll of Honour in the Nurses' War Memorial Chapel in Westminster Abbey.

6 Into the Health Service 1945 – 1958

When the war ended in 1945 the Royal began to make a gradual transition back to peace-time operation. Once again war had accelerated developments in medicine and some of the new drugs had already been used in the hospital with spectacular effect. The first of the new antibacterial drugs – the sulphonomides – had been followed in 1944 by penicillin.[1] With these new weapons and the growing wealth of knowledge more changes were inevitable. History was also to repeat itself in that a new young matron was to lead the nurses into the era of nationalised hospital services.

In the meantime, the Royal's wartime trappings gradually disappeared, as blackout and balcony steps were removed and brick walls demolished. The folding emergency beds were kept, however, as demand for the hospital's services was expected to increase.

The new medical specialties were also clamouring for facilities. But, as materials were as scarce as funds, the Board was in no position to start building. Instead, changes were made by reorganising the existing accommodation and by the use of temporary buildings. The first major new department to be housed was neurosurgery. The Fracture Clinic plaster room was converted into a theatre, and Wards 21 and 22 were later extended to provide both neurosurgical and neurology beds.[2] For the oldest specialty, cardiology, an electrocardiographic department was set up in the old Dispensary – the Dispensary having been dispatched to new premises in the basement. In 1947 space was found for a dietetic department with Miss Barbara Taylor (a nurse dietitian) in charge. Gynaecology patients were transferred to a new Dri-crete building (Wards 23 and 24) off the covered way between the hospital and the New Nurses' Home, and Wards 17 and 18 were given over to fracture and orthopaedic inpatients. This delighted the Fracture Clinic staff, who no longer had to do long treks to attend to their scattered patients. By moving 'gynae' outpatients to a new mezzanine floor in the Extern hall, space was made for an ambulance room, a dressing room and a 'clean' theatre for minor outpatient surgery.[3] Although its appearance had changed, Extern still had the same customers, only more of them. Men from the shipyard still explained how they had injured their toes, 'Drapped the job on me fut doctor'; stitchers from the factories arrived with fingers impaled by the needles of their sewing machines; and hacklers came from the mills, their hands punctured by rows of hackling pins. It was a fascinating and endlessly varied place to work. Finally, in 1957, the first brand new building in the main hospital since the end of the war (Wards 25 and 26) was opened to house metabolic and 'skin' (dermatology) patients.

The long waiting list was reduced by admitting a number of patients to the Throne Hospital for hernia repairs.[4] In 1950 a plastic surgery unit was also opened there. The need for this specialty had been emphasised in 1947, when an engine room explosion in the liner *Reina del Pacifico*, on trials in Belfast Lough, brought a number of serious burns casualties to the Royal. These were treated at first by continuous irrigation with sodium hypochlorite and salt (Milton), using equipment specially flown over from London, but the patients had later to be transferred to East Grinstead in Surrey for plastic surgery.

All this extra work, and the commitment to introduce a forty-eight hour week for all nurses made another nurses' home an urgent priority. A large new one was planned, the first phase of which was opened in 1953 and named after Miss Bostock. As a temporary measure, prefabricated huts were erected in 1946 beside the covered way, providing rooms for ninety-four nurses. Although supervised by staff from the New Nurses' Home, and with only approved nurses being allocated rooms there, 'the huts' were very attractive to wandering medical students and many illicit parties were held. The Medical Superintendent's house was also adapted for use as a nurses' home. Miss Jackson, the Linen Room Supervisor, whose own home had been destroyed in the air raids of 1941, was appointed Warden – the first non-nurse to hold such a post in the Royal. A homely, relaxed atmosphere made Riddel House, as it was now called, a favourite residence until Bostock House was opened, when it was turned into offices for the Group Medical Secretary and his staff.

Temporary rooms were also found in the Throne Hospital, in the

Presbyterian Hostel, and in Lennoxvale, where a house was bought and adapted to house thirty-four night nurses, who were brought to and fro by bus, night and morning. For a time taxis were used instead, one very popular driver being the former world boxing champion Rinty Monaghan.

The introduction of the Health Service on July 1, 1948, was a major turning point in the life of the Royal, as it was for all the other voluntary hospitals. It did more than inject funds where they were desperately needed. For the first time, most hospitals, voluntary and rate–aided, were brought under a single controlling authority,[5] the Northern Ireland Hospitals Authority, which was set up to organise the hospital service throughout the Province. Hospital management committees were appointed to organise the day to day running of, often disparate, groups of hospitals. The Belfast Hospitals Management Committee was formed to take charge of the group of hospitals on the Royal site (RVH,RMH and RBHSC) and the Benn, Belfast Ophthalmic, Throne and Claremont Street Hospitals. For the retiring RVH Board of Management the Health Service came as a great relief, marking the end of its struggle to persuade the public to part with sufficient money to enable the hospital make both ends meet – or at least not let them get too far apart.[6]

The future seemed even rosier in 1949, when a further Act of Parliament was passed at Westminster guaranteeing the finance necessary to bring the health and social services in Northern Ireland up to the standard of those in Britain – an immense task as these services were far in arrears.[7] The necessary improvements entailed a huge outlay on both capital and running costs, and it was not long before those in authority realised that the dream Health Service was costing a great deal more than had been anticipated, and economies were once again called for. Initial budgeting almost certainly had not allowed for the patient, from one of the remoter parts of the Province, who decided that his entitlement to free health service included the hire of a large car to take him to an outpatient department in the Royal and bring his friends to the city for a day's shopping! The Medical Superintendent was stunned when the bill arrived on his desk for repayment.

Outpatients was one of the first areas in the hospital to be affected by the new free Health Service, and the traditional system of accepting anyone who arrived armed with a doctor's letter, many of whom had to sit for hours waiting to be seen, began to collapse as the numbers escalated. The appointment system introduced in 1951 reduced the waiting time – and the crowds – but it was still slow going at times and everyone appreciated the canteen which the Ladies' Committee opened in Extern. In 1954 the Committee also paid for a guide to help patients through the bewildering maze of the expanding Outpatient Department. Her services were so much in demand that further voluntary helpers were recruited. Dressed in pink overalls to make them easily recognisible, they inevitably became known as Pink Ladies.

The Ladies' Committee started life in 1939 as the Association of Friends of the RVH, when it devoted its energies to fund raising. When the Hospitals Authority relieved it of this responsibility in 1948, the Committee at first found itself virtually redundant, but, working in close co-operation with Matron, it turned its attentions to other aspects of the hospital's work, particularly to the comfort and wellbeing of patients and their relatives. It provided an ambulance to transport Fracture Clinic patients who were unable to walk. (As the first driver, Frank, also learned how to make plaster of paris bandages, and helped with the heavy work of removing plasters – until Albert the porter joined the Fracture Clinic staff – he was doubly welcome.) It also helped with refurbishing wards, provided cubicles, and paid for prototypes of innovations, such as tip-up seats for the ward corridors, before hospital funds were used for their general installation. The nurs-

'That will be seven and sixpence please.' Nursing staff at sale of work for Royal College of Nursing Appeal Fund (1951).
(Miss J. McCauley)

ing staff helped the Committee raise funds through sales of work, coffee mornings, bridge drives and jumble sales – the latter being so popular with the local customers that the loaded tables had to be nailed to the floor to protect the helpers from being crushed in the mêlée.

The general appearance of the hospital was made more cheerful when the wards were repainted in colour schemes chosen by the consultants, and the tombstone-like marble commemorative plaques removed and replaced by small brass plates attached to pictures, some of which were donated by the artists themselves. Other pictures were hung on the main corridor and in outpatient departments.

The elimination of noise – exacerbated now by the increase in number of people moving about the hospital who, unlike the nursing staff, did not wear sound-deadening rubber heels on their shoes – received particular attention in these years; wooden doors were replaced with plastic, zinc buckets replaced by rubber, and milk was distributed in cartons instead of cans. Portable screens, which could too easily be knocked over with a heart-stopping crash – particularly when it happened in the middle of the night – were replaced by curtained cubicles. These had the extra benefit of giving the patients more privacy.

Trays or no trays, the plates have still to be scraped. Nurse collecting dirty dishes after dinner, 1950s. (Mrs I. McDonagh, Coleraine)

Other improvements in the 'hotel service' also followed, not directly related to the reduction of noise. Patients who were allowed up were provided with armchairs instead of the old Nightingale couches, and a shop was opened on the main corridor. For the bedbound, the replacement of horsehair mattresses with dunlopillo, the provision of earphones for radio (and later for television), individual call bells and anglepoise lamps, all made their stay more comfortable. The lamps meant that a strict lights out at 8.30 p.m. was no longer necessary and wakeful patients could continue to read without disturbing their neighbours. They were also a great help to night staff for whom, in earlier years, an electric hand lamp, dangled from a screen or hand held, had been the only source of light at the bedside. Another lamp near the door, and a chair and table, provided the night nurse with a base which gave her a view of the whole ward instead of half of it, as had been the case when the her chair was placed under a central pulldown lamp. The presentation of the patients' food was improved. Everyone was given cups and saucers, trays and cruets. A full evening meal replaced the traditional 6.30 p.m. drink or porridge. Shortened daily visiting hours were substituted for the longer four-times-weekly sessions. The entrance hall was furnished as a waiting room for relatives of critically ill patients, an improvement on the long wooden benches of Extern, which was all they had had before.

Time passes slowly in a hospital bed. To help patients through the day, occupational therapy (then simply another name for handcrafts) was started in 1946. A loaded trolley of wool, leather and other materials was wheeled round the wards each week, from which the patients could buy what they wanted at a reduced rate. The women most often chose knitting, but the men tried their hand at different crafts – particularly leather work, both proudly presenting their completed work to family or friends when they came to visit. The service, which was started by Mrs Crawford Brown, was later run by Mrs Webster, mother of the well-known comedienne Leila Webster. With the same cheerful extrovert personality as her daughter, she was a welcome visitor when she appeared in the wards, her small plump figure dwarfed by the loaded trolley.

Not only was the 'hotel' side of hospital care improving, but new drugs and operations were bringing hope of cure or alleviation of many previously incurable diseases. Pneumonia was no longer a killer – nor a source of pride to the nursing staff when a patient was successfully brought through the crisis. Infectious heart disease could often be cured with penicillin; even tuberculosis was now amenable to drug treatment. Drugs and surgery were helping to control dangerously high blood pressure, and cardiac surgery was giving new life to patients with crippling rheumatic heart disease. New diagnostic techniques pin-pointed brain tumours and heart defects in a way not previously possible; and deafness from otosclerosis could now be cured by fenestration. The value of cortisone for crippling rheumatoid arthritis, and other diseases, was being explored; and a better understanding and application of the science of dietetics made a more normal life possible for many diabetics. It was a time of great hope as well as great change.

Changes were occurring for the nurses too. Although clothes rationing continued, nurses' uniforms were exempted. In addition, the restrictions on the amount of material which could be used were lifted and extra coupons were allocated for uniform stockings, so straps reappeared on aprons and bare legs were once more stockinged. (The short sleeves, which had proved to be a practical improvement, were retained.) In 1949, Matron offered all nurses the choice of changing from black to white shoes and stockings – a rare instance of democracy at work in the realm of nurses' uniforms! The 'ayes' had it.[8] Whilst impecunious nurses no longer patronised undertakers' establishments, they sometimes resorted to using lengths of Tubegauz – with a knot tied at the toe – instead of stockings.

The introduction of year badges in 1951 was another small but useful addition to uniform. The choice of colours, green for first year, blue for second and red for third, invited frequent ribald remarks from doctors and medical students – such as 'Greenhorn' or 'Red for danger' – until the value of being able to distinguish a new student nurse from an experienced final year colleague began to be appreciated.

We were sure we had the measurements right! Two newcomers to Preliminary Training School in The Beeches try on their first uniforms. (Mrs V. Fullerton, Co Antrim)

In the mid 1950s the procedure for providing uniform was changed. Instead of nurses being given lengths of material to take on an annual pilgrimage to Mr Jeffries, contractors were employed to make dresses and aprons. Although measurements were provided, the new impersonal service was not without its faults. When the uniforms were delivered, a tall girl might find herself with a mini, while her more petite colleague struggled with a gown apparently designed to fit one of Miss Bostock's nurses – with its hem four inches from the floor.

With changes the order of the day in the Royal, it was fitting that the reins should be handed over to younger people. In 1946 Colonel Langstaff, the Medical Superintendent, was replaced by Brigadier Davidson (The Brig) and Miss Musson by Miss F.E.Elliott. Following her retirement Miss Musson was awarded an MBE and, in 1951, was commemorated in the naming of the New Nurses' Home as Musson House. In her twenty-four years as Matron, annual admissions had risen from 4,000 to 10,000 and she had seen many changes take place, both within the hospital and in the wider field of nursing in Northern Ireland, many of which she had initiated herself.

Tragically, particularly for such a highly intelligent and talented woman, her mental health began to deteriorate after some years in retirement, but she was well enough to see a long-standing wish of hers brought to fruition. Pleased with the success of the annual reunions she had started, Miss Musson had been keen to formalise the links with former and serving Royal nurses. The war, however, had delayed action and it was not until after she retired that her wish was finally granted. On the 26th of April 1949 the Royal Victoria Hospital

League of Nurses was inaugurated and Miss Musson was unanimously elected President, an office she held until her death in 1958. The following year, the first issue of the League's annual magazine was produced. It has kept the worldwide membership in touch with happenings in the hospital and with each other ever since. A benevolent fund was also started with a view to helping former Royal nurses in difficulty. Forty years on, the membership of the League has grown to over a thousand.

An Ulsterwoman takes the reins: Miss F.E. Elliott, Matron 1946–66.
(RVH, Belfast)

Miss Musson's successor, Miss F.E. Elliott, trained in the Royal and was Sister of Wards 7 and 8 before going to Edinburgh to become a midwife and a midwifery sister, returning to Northern Ireland in 1943 as Matron of Whiteabbey Sanitorium. From there she came to the Royal. She was not only the first Royal-trained nurse to hold the post, but the first Ulsterwoman, and did much in a distinguished career to enhance the reputation of nursing both in the hospital and the Province. Ahead of her in 1946 lay the task of steering Royal nursing into the unknown territory of a nationalised health service. She was well suited to the occasion. A woman of vision and great common sense, she set her own guide-lines, for none were given to her on her appointment. Her more informal style was balanced, particularly in the more stressful early years, by occasional flares of a rather unpredictable temper, so that few were foolish enough to question her authority. Throughout her time in office she gave absolute priority to the patient and his or her care, but at the same time tried to ensure that, in providing a first class nursing service, the hospital did not also exploit the learner nurses as it had done for so many years. Unlike previous matrons she was fortunate in that, after 1948, her work was not unduly limited by a shortage of money.

One of the most outwardly-visible differences between the old and the new regimes lay in Miss Elliott's approach to the daily ward round. While Miss Musson had been acutely observant, the passage of years had made her routine round rather monotonous and repetitive. Miss Elliott chose instead to make it a more informal affair, questioning her escort (at times even selecting an appalled junior to accompany her, instead of Sister or a staff nurse) about the patients, speaking to one here and there as she passed. When a system of providing her with a photograph of every new nurse was introduced, Miss Elliott memorised the name of each one within a few days (to the extent that more than forty years later she can still name, with extraordinary accuracy, hundreds of her former nurses) and she expected nurses to be equally meticulous about learning the names of their patients.

As well as having a new matron, the return of demobilised nurses and the introduction of compulsory retirement at sixty-five by the Hospitals Authority, led to many other changes in the nursing staff after the war. Sister Nora Earls returned from the Queen Alexandra'a Imperial Military Nursing Service in 1945 to become Home Sister. Sister K.M. Bell, another Royal-trained nurse, was appointed Sister of Extern, later moving to the new Neurosurgical Unit, where her war-

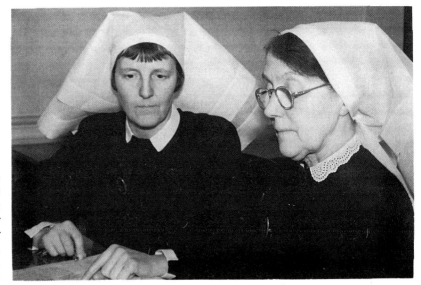

Two of a kind. The retiring Assistant Matron, Miss Montague, hands over to her successor Miss Earls. (*Nursing Times,* London)

time experience in this specialty was put to good use. Several other ex-service nurses were later appointed to sisters' posts as they became vacant. Sister Brown, anticipating compulsory retirement, left in December 1947 aged seventy-two, sadly dying only a few months later in the hospital she had served so faithfully for nearly a quarter of a century.[9] Miss Montague, who, with her calm common sense and long experience, had been a tower of strength to the new Matron, retired in 1950. She was succeeded as Assistant Matron by Miss Earls, whom most people saw as a modern Monty, wise, practical and kind. A second assistant matron, Miss Mary Scott, was also appointed. A gentle, very private person, and a dedicated nurse, Miss Scott had previously been Sister in Wards 3 and 4, and Home Sister of the New Nurses' Home. Two years later Sister Steele retired as Home Sister and was replaced by the kindly Miss E.L. Duff. Miss Earls was then promoted to the newly-created post of Deputy Matron and Miss M.A. McFarland appointed Assistant Matron in her place. Like all the senior staff at this time, 'Mac' had trained in the Royal. Appointed Sister of Wards 11 and 12 in 1939, she later took charge of the new Fracture Clinic, leaving to become Assistant Matron of Whiteabbey Hospital before returning to the same post in the Royal.

In 1953 Sister Dynes retired, most reluctantly, aged seventy-five, having been retained since 1948 at the request of the Hospital Management Committee and with the consent of the Hospitals Authority even though she was then seventy years old.[10] With her went the last link with the pre-World War One years, for she was the last of Miss Bostock's nurses to work in the hospital. Shortly before her retirement, on the recommendation of Mr (later Sir) Ian Fraser, one of the consultant surgeons, she was awarded an MBE, a hugely popular recognition of forty-four years unbroken service on night duty. When the award was announced, the housemen made a large plaster of paris 'MBE' and went in search of Diana to present it to her. Frustrated in their search, they resorted to hanging it round the neck of another great lady – the statue of Queen Victoria in the quadrangle, completing the ornamentation in the traditional manner by crowning Her Majesty with a bedpan. Sister Dynes was succeeded as Night Superintendent first by Miss Agnes Campbell, and in 1955 by her Junior Night Sister Miss Hazel Gaw, who was to hold the office for twenty-three years, and also become one of the great nursing personalities of the hospital.

1953 was a momentous year in the Royal for a number of reasons other than the retirement of Sister Dynes. In the early weeks two major catastrophes touched the hospital. Following an air crash at Nutt's Corner Airport, the dead and injured were brought to the hospital, including one of its own medical students (fortunately not seriously injured); and although only one casualty was admitted following the sinking of the Larne-Stranraer ferry *Princess Victoria* (when 133 lives were lost), a number of the hospital's doctors were called upon to stand by, to help wherever necessary. It was Coronation year too, when television appeared in the Royal for the first time – hired for the occasion to enable staff and ambulant patients see the historic event. It was also the fiftieth anniversary of the hospital on the Grosvenor Road site, and this was celebrated with a service of thanksgiving and re-dedication in the newly-opened Bostock House, which was also the venue for a colourful and well-attended Jubilee ball.

As the work of the hospital continued to grow, it became increasingly obvious that the traditional dual role of the Matron, as head nurse cum housekeeper, was far too much for one person. The obvious solution was to delegate. So chores such as the supervison of the Laundry, the ordering of food and supplies, the annual stocktaking, and the weekly checking of breakages, were handed over to a laundry manager and to catering and supplies officers (one of the features of the Health Service was the proliferation of 'officers'). A domestic supervisor took charge of the domestic staff. While all these individuals were responsible to the Medical Superintendent rather than Matron, Miss Elliott nevertheless retained close contact with all departments on behalf of the nursing service. On one occasion, for example, she dissuaded the Supplies Officer from buying shorter sheets by pointing out that this would be a false economy; not only would it be less comfortable for the patients, but it would make needless work for nurses, as short ends constantly came untucked. She was also given secretarial help, a most important addition to her staff in view of the massive increase in paper work which the Health Service occasioned.

Matron was not the only person carrying a heavier load. To help with the work in some of the more rapidly expanding departments a number of extra sisters' posts were created. Because of the increasing complexity of theatre work a full time theatre sister was appointed in 1948, with responsibility for two theatres. Others followed and finally, in 1957, at the request of the consultant surgeons, a sister was appointed to each theatre – with the exception of Ophthalmics. In 1950, a sister with responsibility for theatre work was added to the night staff, releasing the Junior Night Sister for other duties. In 1949 when Extern was divided into Casualty and Outpatients, a second sister was appointed; another was appointed to the Dermatology Outpatient Department, and a second, part-time, sister to the Venereology Department.

'And tell me Miss Elliott, do you remember the 'useless' nurse you had when you were Sister in 15 and 16?' Matron, chatting to Miss Elizabeth Elliott, former Matron of Belfast Ophthalmic Hospital at a meeting of the Nurses' League. (Miss M.K. Robb, Dundonald)

More part-time nurses were used in the outpatient departments as the number of patients and morning clinics increased. Miss Elliott was unhappy about using student nurses for prolonged periods in work which was of little training value, and insisted that none of them should remain in one of these departments for more than three months. The new regulation invited the displeasure of some consultants, Dr J.T.Lewis in particular. When a student nurse had learned the ropes of his clinic he expected her to remain there for a long time, but if a new nurse displeased him he would turn to his house physician and say, 'Take a good look at that nurse – you won't be seeing *her* again'. Whereupon he would repair to Matron's office and demand his previous nurse back. By introducing permanent, part-time, trained nurses to these clinics, Miss Elliott found a solution that satisfied everyone.

More help was also forthcoming for the ward sisters. In 1954, junior sisters were appointed. (Distinguished later by a navy uniform dress, the two grades became known as red and blue sisters.) The Junior Sister relieved her senior of much of her teaching responsibilities and deputized for her when she was off duty or on holiday. Some units were later allocated two or more blue sisters.

The introduction of a monthly meeting between Matron and the sisters gave both parties an opportunity to air and discuss ideas, plans, problems and grievances – although, almost inevitably, Matron's viewpoint on most questions was acceded to with little dissent! In time, similar meetings were held with each grade of nursing staff.

While these meetings could be helpful, they did not compensate for inadequate training for the job. Nurses were appointed to sisters' posts with nothing but their own experience to guide them. The value of this experience was governed entirely by chance. The lucky ones had worked in wards with competent ward sisters, the unlucky ones had not. Partly to remedy this deficiency, and partly to combat any tendency to parochialism, Miss Elliott used an annual £1,000 allowance given to her by the Hospitals Authority to send staff to other parts of the United Kingdom on courses in subjects as diverse as neurosurgery, plastic surgery, dermatology and venereology. (Miss Musson had also done this but had been severely restricted by lack of funds.) A better understanding of administrative skills was also fostered by sending younger sisters to a ward sisters' course run locally by the Royal College of Nursing.

The Hospitals Authority was also persuaded to give grants for longer courses, and several nurses were sent on tutor training courses in Great Britain – a qualification not then obtainable in Northern Ireland. Miss Kathleen Acheson was also sent to train as a dietitian, returning in 1948 to work in the Dietetic Department, and becoming Senior Dietitian when Miss Taylor left.

Miss Elliott was adept at tracking down scholarships and bursaries which could be used to widen the experience of her staff. In 1948, one staff nurse was awarded the Student Nurses Association Halford Bursary to study nursing in Denmark for a month, in 1950, another obtained a World Health Organisation scholarship to study nursing in Paris for six months, and in 1958 the Principal Tutor, Miss Elizabeth Mitchell, was given leave of absence for a year to take up a Rockefeller Foundation Scholarship at Columbia University in the United States.

Matron, having disposed of many of her own non-nursing duties, and arranged help for her sisters, started to look at the duties of the student nurses to see what could be done for them. One of her first actions was to reduce their domestic work. The weekly chore of table-

If it's dishes, it must be Sunday. Washing dishes on the wardsmaid's evening off. (Dr P. Donaldson, Dundonald)

scrubbing was dispensed with by covering the tables with laminated plastic, and extra porters were employed to carry bins – no more forgetful nurses running laden to the corridor to catch the morning collection. The first theatre orderly (male) was appointed in 1946 to the neurosurgical theatre, and the first ward orderly arrived in 1957. Dressed in a distinctive pale yellow overall, she relieved the nurses of dusting, locker-cleaning, distributing drinks, and some bed-making.[11]

Labour-saving devices saved further time. Centrally sterilized blood transfusion sets saved time previously spent in preparation and in sterilizer watching – in case some one should inadvertently add un-sterile material to its bubbling contents. The Pharmacy (formerly the Dispensary) provided prepared dressings for autoclaving, which not only saved time but prevented the callouses which resulted from hacking through endless layers of gauze with steadily blunting scissors.

Although a forty-eight, and from 1948, a forty-four hour week had been promised to nurses, lack of accommodation for the extra staff needed to introduce shorter hours made this difficult to achieve. As each new batch of bedrooms was acquired, the gain seemed to be cancelled by the need to employ extra nurses for expanding departments. So, seven years after the promise had been made, most nurses still worked more than forty-eight hours each week, although the reduction in domestic duties had made some increase in off duty and holidays possible. In 1947, annual leave for all nurses was increased from three to four weeks and, in 1948, staff nurses as well as sisters were given a long morning off on alternate Sundays. Night nurses were allowed two nights off after six on duty in summer as well as winter (instead of one night off after five). In 1956, the starting time for day nurses was put forward from 7 a.m. to 7.15 a.m., and later to 7.45 a.m. In the following year, by employing more non-resident staff it became possible to increase the daily off-duty hours and finally, in 1957, a forty-four hour week was achieved.

The four-year contract was reduced again to three shortly after Miss Elliott's appointment as Matron. She asked for this as she believed it was totally wrong to exploit the nurses in this way. The Committee agreed, but insisted that existing fourth year nurses (whose salaries were immediately increased to staff nurses' scale) should give three months notice in order to avoid sudden shortages of staff. The new system had its advantages in that Matron could now invite selected qualifiers to stay to gain experience, but was under no obligation to keep the rest.

In July 1948 pay for nurses throughout the United Kingdom was put on an equal scale for the first time. Parity for pensions took a little longer, but complete reciprocity was achieved by 1956. The first pay rise in 1949 was fairly substantial, with ward sisters rising from a scale of £160 – £220 a year to £245 – £370; staff nurses from £120 – £160 to £195 – £295; and student nurses from £55 – £75 to £100 – £125.

The Rushcliffe Report (and the Woodside Report of 1946 which had dealt with local pay and conditions) had pressed for a relaxation of off duty restrictions, and for improvements in conditions in the nurses' homes. As a result, a hairdressing salon, a visitors' room (it was still strictly forbidden for nurses to entertain guests in their rooms – even parents!) and tea-making facilities were added to Musson House. There was some easing of the rules too, particularly after the older staff had retired, although a nurse's dusting of her bedroom could still be tested by the inspecting Home Sister recording the date in the dust on the top of the wardrobe and presenting the irrefutable evidence to the occupant at a later date!

Shorter working hours also gave nurses more leisure time and badminton, tennis, hockey and swimming continued to be popular. In 1951, a choir of nurses and doctors, under Sister Rita Roulstone, gave a carol concert in aid of the Royal College of Nursing's Appeal Fund. In spite of the fact that the musical ability of some of the choristers was modest to say the least – one had to mime the top notes in some of the pieces – Sister Roulstone courageously included the *Hallelujah Chorus* from Handel's *Messiah* in the programme. Her faith was rewarded. Not only was the concert a success but the choir became a hospital institution and later made several records. A branch of the Nurses Christian Fellowship was also set up. It was then organised locally by a Royal-trained nurse, Jean Anderson, who later worked as a missionary in Thailand, continuing to serve there after becoming severely disabled by poliomyelitis. A branch of the Presbyterian Girls' Auxiliary also attracted a number of members.

Important changes were made in the field of staff health care. Although the Student Nurses Association (an increasingly vocal spokesbody for its members) has asked for a lady doctor to succeed Dr Foster Coates as the nurses' doctor when he retired in 1945, Dr Howard Crozier was appointed. In 1948, however, he was given a lady assistant, Dr Margaret Campbell. She eventually succeeded Dr Crozier, and under her kindly supervision, attitudes towards sick nurses were transformed. No longer were most afraid to report sick until unable to avoid doing so, in case they should incur the displeasure, if not the wrath, of the senior nursing staff. Annual medical inspections for all student nurses were organised, and any nurse who

*'I think there should
be enough for all of
us!' Miss Musson cuts
the Student Nurses
Association's 21st
birthday cake.*
(source unknown)

had a positive reaction to the routine tuberculin test was sent home for
three months, even if she showed no symptoms of tuberculosis. The
improving health of nurses, helped by the reduction in working hours
and by physical training classes (run by the Physiotherapy Department), was reflected in falling numbers reporting sick with boils,
septic fingers or tonsillitis. Dr Campbell was opposed to leaving sick
nurses in their rooms but it was often difficult to find beds for them in
busy wards, although ward sisters were unfailingly helpful if they had
room. More than once, beds normally used by venereology patients
had to be pressed into service! When the new gynaecology wards
were opened, an annex was allocated as a nurses' sick bay; but
acquisitive gynaecologists soon took it into the main unit and sick
nurses were again homeless until they were given the beds in Wards
21 and 22, vacated when the new Dermatology Ward opened.

Like Miss Musson, Miss Elliott was always ready to suggest or
support innovations, and she quickly established excellent relations
with the staff of the school. At her suggestion the Principal Tutor was
invited to attend meetings of the Nursing Committee and was included
in the selection of candidates for training.

As before, acceptance – to an extent – hung on the personal

interview with Matron, or one of her assistants, and the Principal
Tutor. Most candidates were from Northern Ireland or the Republic,
but in 1950 two Nigerian girls were accepted. This was quite a novelty
for both nurses and patients, but the girls were warmly welcomed and
settled happily into hospital life.[12] Although they were English-speak-
ing, the local idiom at first gave them some problems. One of them
recalls her first evening on the wards when she was sent to refill the
patients' teacups. She asked, 'Does anyone want more tea?' and one
man held out his cup. While it was being replenished, his neighbour
said, 'Gi'es a wee drop too'. Baffled, she retreated to the kitchen to ask
the staff nurse how she could get 'a wee drop' out of the very large
brown enamel teapot! The relative rarity of coloured faces in Northern
Ireland at that time was the cause of a slight misunderstanding on
another occasion, when the second Nigerian nurse was sent to stay
with a patient recovering from anaesthetic. Sister, arriving just after the
patient regained consciousness, was rather surprised to be greeted
with, 'Thank goodness to see you Sister – I thought I had died and was
in heaven!' The dark face of Nurse Grillo (whom he had not previously seen) bending over him had startled him, but her cheerful smile,
he felt, could not possibly be connected with 'the other place'.

As the hospital had no recruitment problem, many who were
accepted for training had to wait for a vacancy. For these, and for
others who still had doubts about taking up nursing, several alternatives were offered, which helped winnow out those whose talents lay
elsewhere. They could apply to a specialist hospital for a shorter
training, perhaps in fever or tuberculosis nursing, or they could work
for a while in a smaller general hospital such as Lagan Valley to 'test
the water'. A number were taken into the Royal itself where, for a
small payment and free board and lodging, they helped the nurses
with simpler duties. They were officially designated general nursing
assistants but, because they wore blue overalls, were better known as
Bluecoats.

In 1946 steps were taken to expand the block training, at this time
limited to a week off for revision before final. Extra revision time was
given before both state examinations, but the real step forward was
when second year nurses were taken from the wards into the school
for two weeks to study advanced nursing techniques. This included
teaching rounds in the wards with the clinical sisters, and was the the
first real link to be established between ward and classroom.

The Principal Tutor, Miss Kate Huey, resigned in 1950, and was
succeeded by her assistant, Miss Elizabeth Mitchell. Miss Mitchell was
the school's first fully qualified tutor and she approached the study of

nursing from a much more academic angle than her predecessors. Some nurses found this different approach too difficult, and for a period there was an unexpectedly high dropout rate. The rest, however, adapted successfully under Miss Mitchell's supervision and helped by her excellent teaching.

Nurse training had been lagging behind the rapid developments in medical treatment. New skills had to be learnt in the ward instead of the classroom. The Student Nurses Association, exasperated that its members had to learn obsolete procedures such as surgical fomentations, cupping, non plaster of paris splinting and leeches (which appear to have come into their own again in the late 1980s!) appealed to the Joint Council to have the curriculum updated. Little effective change was made in the official curriculum, but there were some additions made in the RVH school. From 1950 every student nurse had to prepare a case history each year; lessons in floral art were added in 1956;[13] and for a period, each nurse had to make a five-minute speech to her classmates – and Matron! However, this was discontinued as the Principal Tutor felt it required too much time-consuming research. In fact it had rapidly become the custom for outgoing students to leave their speeches under their pillows for their successors, so a useful way of promoting self-confidence was prematurely ended.

The range of student nurses' practical experience was also widened. Previously, in addition to the mandatory periods in medical, surgical and gynaecological wards, and in theatre, each had spent time in a specialist department – eye, ear, nose and throat diseases; orthopaedics; or dermatology. It had rarely been possible for nurses to have experience of more than one specialty, but now third year nurses were sent as observers for a week to each of the specialist departments where they had not previously worked. Further specialist experience in psychiatric, tuberculosis, fever or ophthalmic nursing in other hospitals, for up to three months, was also offered to selected volunteers. Surprisingly, although experience in nursing sick children was mandatory for the General Register, no attempt was made to include it.

In 1947 the Joint Council gave the Royal permission to accept male student nurses. Until this time, only the Belfast City Hospital had accepted men for general nurse training. (Traditionally their work had been in mental nursing.) It was some years before the first man was accepted for full training, but in 1948 four registered mental nurses began the shortened training for the General Register.[14] One of them later described how he and his colleagues had realised that they were, in a sense, ambassadors for their sex in the hitherto exclusively female world of RVH nursing. The men, who were tactfully housed outside

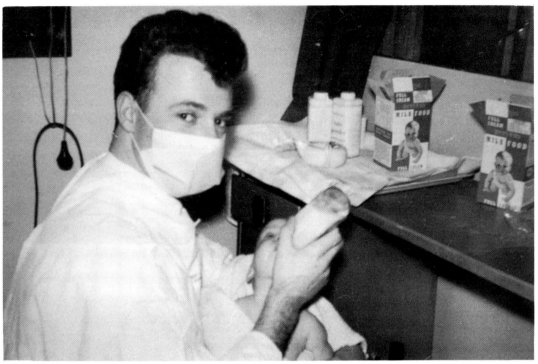

'Who says nursing is women's work?' Nurse Jackie Carville feeds a baby in ward 21 (1963). (Mr J. Carville, RVH)

the hospital, (the nurses' homes were still strictly 'ladies only') soon made a niche for themselves and fully justified the experiment. Far from introducing unwelcome problems, the men, all older by a number of years than their female colleagues, found themselves being mothered in the most kindly fashion. In 1957 the first coloured male nurse, another Nigerian, Moses Inyang, was accepted for training.

With more nurses being withdrawn from the wards for block study in the school, extra space was needed. The Beeches, a large house in Hampton Park, was bought and equipped as a preliminary training school and, in December 1950, the first group of twenty-five nurses took up residence with Miss Geraldine Creighton – a nurse tutor – and a housekeeper in charge.[15]

For those who were fortunate enough to start their training there, the Beeches period was a happy one, successfully bridging the gap between school and hospital – a far cry from the days when lone probationers were catapulted straight on to the wards on their first morning. Less formal than the main school of nursing, it formed a close-knit community until the whole school was reunited in 1965. The period in PTS was lengthened after it transferred to the Beeches, and in each of their last three weeks the student nurses spent two full days in the wards getting acclimatised. Although distant, the PTS was not isolated from the main school. Miss Mitchell visited to lecture on the history of nursing and Matron, who gave each group a welcoming talk on arrival, returned later to give two lectures on ethics.

With the exodus to The Beeches, room became available in Musson House for an extension in block training. Both second and third year nurses were now relieved of ward duties for six weeks, and it was no longer necessary for lectures to be held or much studying done in off duty hours. This was a great relief for student nurses for whom the conquest of sleep in the pursuit of learning had always been a problem. To lie on bed without falling asleep over their notes or textbook was impossible. Some could even doze over on a hard chair. Others, in desperation as examinations loomed, tried to concentrate by sitting on the bare wooden floor, hoping that the draught and the discomfort caused by the beading of the wardrobe sticking into their backs would keep them awake – it didn't!

Miss Elliott, like Miss Musson, was an active member of the Royal College of Nursing, both at local and national level. She served on the Executive of the Northern Ireland Committee for many years, and was appointed as its Chairman in 1948. She was also a member of the National Board of the College, and was one of the few nurses to be actively involved with both the College and the Joint Council – a gap not often bridged at that time. In 1964 Miss Elliott became the first nurse to be appointed Chairman of the Council, a position she held concurrently with the Chairmanship of the Belfast Branch of the College.

The appointment of the dynamic Miss Mona Grey as Secretary and Area Organiser of the RCN in Northern Ireland, in the same year as Miss Elliott became Matron of the Royal, brought a new vitality to the work of the College, and more nurses began to take part in the affairs of their professional body, including its Student Nurses Association. The RVH Unit celebrated its twenty-first birthday in 1948 with Miss Musson, its founder,as guest of honour. In 1949, Nurse Mary Gribbon was one of six student nurses from the United Kingdom to represent the Association in Sweden at the International Council of Nurses Conference. In 1947, the winner of the first speech-making competition for student nurses in Northern Ireland was a Royal nurse, Doreen McEwan.[16] The following year another Royal nurse, Alexandra Smyth, not only won the Baird Cup but went on to national level to win the Cates Shield, an achievement repeated four years later by Nurse Nuala Kenny.

The urgent need to provide a better local base for the College – which was an important centre for post-graduate training – led to the

establishment of an appeals committee in 1949, under the chairmanship of Mrs Robert Marshall, wife of one of the Royal's consultant physicians. The Committee had the seemingly impossible task of raising
£50,000 within four years.[17] Pageants, plays, sales and concerts, were
organised, and Royal nurses participated at every level, from starring
as Florence Nightingale in a pageant (Olive Daly) to acting as humble
dressers behind the scenes or bargaining with potential customers at
jumble sales. But the target was achieved, and the new College head-
quarters was opened in College Gardens in 1954.

One sad feature of these years was the erosion of the feeling of
community which had hitherto characterised life in the Royal, when
most of those working in it – nurses, doctors, radiographers, maids,
cooks, clerical, administrative and maintenance staff – knew, or at
least recognised each other. Now, with the huge proliferation of staff
and the growth of new buildings which drew many away from the
heart of the hospital, strange faces abounded and contacts with familiar ones were weakening or being lost.

Although the Health Service crock of gold had proved to be shal-
lower than anticipated, in its first decade the improvements in, and
expansion of, every aspect of work in the Royal Victoria Hospital had
been considerable. Miss Elliott had proved to be another innovative
and progressive matron, who had the bonus, denied to her predecessors, of adequate funds to carry out her projects. Even more radical
changes for nursing lay ahead in the second part of her reign.

7 Expansion and Innovation 1958 – 1966

The 1950s and 1960s were decades of expansion. In the late 1950s hopes were high that before too long the old Royal would be replaced by a new hospital. Between 1964 and 1966 the hospital Capital Works Project Team worked out detailed plans, but the Hospitals Authority was unable to undertake the project because of the urgent needs of other hospitals, many of which had buildings that were much older than those of the Royal.[1]

So the growth continued to be piecemeal. In 1959 a small respiratory failure unit was set up in Ward 22. In the same year the Broadway Damask Company's mill was bought and adapted to house the Group Sterile Supply Department (GSSD), a staff sports centre and the School of Physiotherapy. In 1964 a new theatre block was opened with Miss Catherine McQ. Galbraith as its first Theatre Superintendent.

The new theatres were a great improvement. The traffic on the ward corridor had been a problem for the old theatres especially when the doors were left ajar in hot weather, with only a screen hiding the interior from passers by. Not only was there a risk of contamination, but fascinated relatives or even patients waiting for admission could sometimes glimpse the theatre staff at work. For those whose knowledge of an operating theatre was gleaned from novels or the television screen, the *apparently* casual attitude of some of the surgeons must have come as a disappointingly undramatic eye-opener. To hear snippets of a discussion on the previous Saturday's rugby international was disillusion enough, but it must have been even more of a shock if they spotted an anaesthetist sipping calmly at a cup of tea as he administered the anaesthetic. (In case any reader should be getting apprehensive, rest assured, the relaxed atmosphere reflected the team's experience not its indifference.)

Patients were brought to the new theatres in their own beds (the surgical wards having been equipped with mobile Swedish beds) before being transferred to theatre trolleys. After the operation they were returned to their beds but, because the theatres were some distance from the wards, they remained for a time in the theatre recovery ward. To avoid confusion, both patients and beds were labelled. (The following year most members of the hospital staff were similarly labelled, identification badges having become necessary with the proliferation of anonymous individuals wearing white coats – long since abandoned as the doctors' prerogative.)

A new eye, ear, nose and throat clinic (Wards 27 - 31) was opened in 1964, which included the hospital's first children's ward. It combined the work of the Royal with that of the Benn and Belfast Ophthalmic Hospitals,[2] and the former Matron of the Ophthalmic Hospital, Miss Jean McCauley, was put in charge, with the rank of assistant matron.

Several of the Eye and Ear Clinic's innovations were of particular interest to the nursing staff. Laundry and garbage were collected in paper sacks (later introduced throughout the hospital) and disposed of via chutes. Its Ganymede meal service gave patients a choice of dishes, with main courses served on covered plates kept warm by heated tablets. Finally, nurses' uniforms were updated by discarding the traditional white apron.

In 1965 the Dental Department was moved yet again, this time to the custom-built School of Dentistry. A small nursing staff under Sister D.E.N.Morrow was appointed to look after patients having minor surgery.[3] This was quite a change from the days when the only nurse in Dental was a junior seconded on weekday mornings to the extraction room. It had been a popular posting, as not only was she virtually unsupervised but the extractions were mostly done by young dental students.

The West Wing dining room was given to the ECG Department, which had already invaded this hitherto sacrosanct nursing territory in 1960, when the nurses sitting room had been taken over for angiocardiography. Eventually it acquired the entire ground floor, and Matron's Office and the Home Office were rehoused beside East Wing.

Cardiology was another rapidly expanding specialty – helped no doubt by Northern Ireland's leading position in world rankings of death from heart disease. A coronary care unit was set up in Wards 5 and 6 in 1963. By watching a central monitor screen, nurses could now immediately identify patients in need of attention. Piped medical gases, including oxygen, which had been installed throughout the hospital a few years earlier, were another very useful asset. Relief was available at the turn of a tap, instead of having to wait for a porter to trundle a cumbersome oxygen cylinder up from the store.

In 1966, there was another great step forward in the treatment of heart disease when Dr (later Professor) J.F.Pantridge, with the help of a British Heart Foundation grant, inaugurated the world's first cardiac ambulance service at the hospital; a life-saving enterprise which has since been copied worldwide. Each ambulance team includes a staff nurse – the first time nurses have been sent outside the hospital to work. With a cardiac ambulance service now covering most of the Province, it is ironic that Northern Ireland, with its appalling level of heart disease, has now become one of the safest places to have a heart attack.

Inevitably, with an increasing number of patients in the hospital and a decreasing working week for nurses (by 1960 down to forty-four hours, and by 1966 down to forty-two), more staff accommodation was needed. Although the second phase of Bostock House was completed in 1960, providing another seventy-seven bedrooms for nurses, with a large restaurant added four years later, demand continued to outstrip supply, and in 1963 plans were made to build a block of flats at lower Broadway, the first such flats for nurses in Northern Ireland.[4] Broadway Tower proved to be a very successful venture and plans were made for a second block, Victoria Tower, which was opened in 1969. By this time, with so many nurses living out, Musson House was made virtually redundant as a nurses' home, although still the quarters of the school. West Wing had long since been abandoned. Lennoxvale, which was no longer needed for housing nurses, was sold to Queen's University.

Busier than Central Station. At work in the Nurses Station. Note, through the window, a nurse at work in the ward. (Nursing Times, London)

Meantime, work continued on the wards on the main corridor. The kitchens were modernised. Brown painted shelves were replaced by cupboards, and chipped 'jawbox' sinks[5] by stainless steel. The old refrigerators were replaced and dishwashers added later. Major updating of the surgical wards included the addition of a soundproofed nurses' station which breached the party wall and gave a clear view of both wards. A shower room, extra washhand basins and toilets were added, and the redundant theatre was divided to provide a consultant's office and a dressing room with doors wide enough to wheel bed-bound patients in for treatment. Each side ward was converted into two single rooms. Several years later the medical wards were also updated, with individual variations to suit the specialties involved. Coloured quilts helped soften the stark look of the wards. These were welcomed by all the consultants except Mr Greer, who, because his opinion had not been asked, refused to have the pink quilts chosen for his gynaecology patients. His quilts stayed white. More hygienic cellular cotton blankets replaced wool, and as these shed less fluff they greatly pleased the domestic staff.

A number of changes made life more comfortable for the patients. Balcony awnings, installed in 1960, gave welcome shade in good weather. Disposable polythene sheets replaced the rubber mackintoshes, for years an ordeal for the patients who had to lie on them, and a nuisance for the nurses who had to try to keep the thick red rubber wrinkle free. The introduction of uri-bags meant that patients with self-retaining catheters were no longer confined to bed.

Meal times were brightened by the appearance of colour-banded crockery, and crested paper napkins (the gift of the Ladies Committee). Cooked breakfasts were provided for all from 1960, starting with boiled eggs – which had previously been available, but only if patients provided the eggs. Then, having carefully inscribed the owners' names and cooking instructions in pencil on the shells, the harassed junior nurse had tried to cook them according to request. All too often a pot of egg bullets was all she could offer – with apologies – other more urgent tasks having intervened.

With their surroundings made more attractive and their physical comfort and meals seen to, attention was turned to other aspects of the patients' wellbeing. In a continuing campaign against noise, ward kitchens as well as nurses' stations were soundproofed, and new types of floor covering tested for sound-deadening effect and ease of maintenance. A four-bed night admission unit for surgical patients was opened in 1966, bringing welcome relief for patients in the emergency take-in wards, where sleep was frequently interrupted by new arrivals. Those who needed surgery were sent direct to the theatre, then remained in the Admission Unit until morning. In 1963 an internal radio station – Radio Royal – was inaugurated, which provided both entertainment and spiritual comfort. Its daily epilogue service at 9.15 p.m. replaced the Sunday evening round of ward hymn-singing by the voluntary Sunshine Singers. Although the Singers had given pleasure to many over the years, there were occasions when the presence of acutely ill patients made their visits inopportune, and the new epilogue was available to all who wished to listen. To reduce the sense of isolation from family and friends, mobile telephones (equipped for outgoing calls only) were installed.

There was thought too for patients' relatives and friends. The entrance hall waiting room was carpeted and refurbished. The best available carpeting happened to be orange, so paintwork was chosen to tone, and the hall, its black and white tiles no longer visible, inevitably became known as The Orange Hall!

The introduction of disposable and ready sterilised equipment was welcomed by both patients and nurses. For the former, disposable syringes and needles meant an end to the misery caused by blunt or hooked needles. For the latter, it eliminated a number of traditional nursing chores, and the time spent cleaning and sterilising equipment and packing dressing drums for autoclaving was saved. The most popular of the disposables was almost certainly the sputum mug. In spite of its obvious advantages, however, considerable tact and guile had to be used by Matron and the ward sisters concerned to get it accepted by some ultra-conservative consultants.

Miss Elliott continued to try to reduce the non-nursing duties of her staff. In 1960 ward clerks were employed to help the sisters, and all attempts by medical staff to poach or borrow them were firmly rebuffed by Matron, who kept a vigilant watch on their progress. (The Kardex system of record-keeping further reduced the clerical work, by making written day and night reports, bedbathing and treatment books unnecessary). Other newcomers helped with the simpler nursing tasks. State enrolled nurses were introduced, most of them in the Eye and Ear Clinic and on night duty, and ward assistants were also added to the night staff.[6]

While many traditional chores were being delegated to new workers, much of the traditional pattern of nursing work remained unchanged until 1964, when a detailed survey was undertaken by the

One chore that could go. Nurses sorting clean laundry sometime in the 1950s. This work was later taken over by the laundry staff.
(Mrs I. McDonagh, Coleraine)

Principal Tutor Miss A.P.I.Logan and an assistant matron, Miss D. McCullough. The survey recorded the work of all grades of day and night staff – who did what, with whom and when. It led to a host of improvements. For example, nurses' meal times were changed so that more of them would be available when patients needed help with their meals. It had also been noted that nurses' timetables involved giving drug injections at the end of their shift – at 7 p.m. and 7 a.m. – when they were tired and most likely to make mistakes. By changing injection times to 10 a.m. and 10 p.m. this pitfall was avoided. Night nurses swopped patient washing for the day nurses' serving of breakfast, which ended the overlap of breakfast and bedmaking and the juggling act necessary if the two were to be carried out simultaneously without mishap. Internal rotation replaced the annual three month period of night duty. With nurses now doing both day and night duty in the same ward, patients had the reassurance of familiar faces, and nurses were no longer suddenly confronted with a wardful of strangers when they changed duty. The new arrangements proved rather traumatic for some of the older ward sisters, and great tact had to be used to get them accepted.

There were now many more staff nurses in the hospital than ever before, but the Joint Council, which carried out its first inspection in 1959, was not satisfied that the number in most of the wards was adequate to supervise the student nurses. As the Council had the power to suspend recognition of the Royal as a training school, its warning had to be taken seriously. Efforts were made to recruit more trained staff, and an appeal was made to former Royal nurses to return to either full or part time work. Newly qualified staff nurses were encouraged to stay on for a while, and as an added inducement they were given the option of choosing where in the hospital they would prefer to work. (An interesting side-effect of this new freedom of choice was an improvement in the behaviour of sisters in the most unpopular areas!).

Staffing levels came under the microscope again in 1966 following the tragic and unexpected death one night of a young patient. At the inquest the Coroner raised the question of negligence and ordered an inquiry to be held. Its report totally exonerated the hospital, but recommended that the number of night staff should be increased. As a result, a fourth member (often a ward assistant) was added to the complement of each ward unit, extra night sisters were appointed and the Night Superintendent was given a radio-pager or 'bleep'.

All these changes added considerably to the workload of Matron and her administrative staff, so two extra assistant matrons were ap-

'And this is where you will be the year after next, nurses.' Miss McCullough explains the new allocation system. The allocations board is in the background. (Belfast Telegraph)

pointed in 1963. Miss D.McCullough, formerly Sister in Wards 11 and 12, returned from St George's Hospital in London, where she had seen a new system of nurse allocation in action, to set up a similar system in the Royal. Miss M.K.Robb, formerly a sister in the Fracture Clinic, returned from her post as Matron of Tower Hill Hospital in Armagh to become Nurse Planning Officer on the Capital Works Project Team, then working on plans for the new hospital.

Her appointment to the Capital Works Project Team was something of a breakthrough. Previously those responsible for planning new departments had not considered it necessary to consult the nursing staff, even when nurses were to be responsible for the day to day running of the department when it opened. The first breach in the predominantly medical opposition to nurses entering the corridors of power had come in 1960, when a group matrons' committee (RVH, RMH, and RBHSC) had been formed, its chair taken by each matron in turn. The Group Management Committee was asked if it would permit the Chairman of the Matrons' Committee to attend its meetings when there were matters of nursing interest on the agenda. (Before this, the Matron of the Royal had not attended the Management Committee's meetings, and nursing matters were dealt with by the Medical Superintendent). Some members were opposed to this break with tradition, particularly the Group Medical Superintendent (formerly the Medical Superintendent of the Royal). When Miss Elliott, the first Chairman of the Matrons' Committee, arrived by invitation to the next meeting of the Management Committee, she had the indignity of having to wait in the anteroom while the Group Superintendent fought hard, but unsuccessfully, to have the invitation revoked.[7]

Attitudes were changing within the nursing hierarchy as well. The young women and men – still few in number – entering nursing in the 1950s and 1960s were less prepared to accept restrictions on their off duty hours, and tended to be less deferential towards their seniors. While no less courteous than their predecessors they could see no reason, for example, in holding a door open for a staff nurse approaching from fifty yards away, nor did the staff nurse of the 1960s expect them to. Their contemporaries outside were enjoying the Swinging Sixties – why shouldn't they?

Discipline was becoming less strict. A modest amount of make-up was allowed on duty, although an excess could result in the guilty party being sent to remove it. If nurses could err in judging what was acceptable, so could Matron. One day she spied a nurse wearing what appeared to her to be an excess of mascara, and without waiting for explanation, sent the offender to wash it off – an impossible task as the colour was entirely natural!

Even though discipline was easing, it was still too restrictive for some independent spirits. The most determined defied authority by leaving or entering the nurses' homes by convenient windows, parapets, drainpipes or basements to attend forbidden parties. The small window above a flat roof in Musson House left open for the purpose proved too much one evening for a rather plump nurse, who returned late from a party with some friends. Using a boyfriend's car to reach the roof, a few of the girls had aready climbed in when their more ample friend stuck fast and could not be budged. Everyone still outside climbed on to the roof, formed a chain and pulled. With one final heave they got her out, but not without a few bruises all round as her sudden release sent them all tumbling into a heap. The poor victim had then to go alone to the door and ring for admission while her slimmer friends slipped in through the window. They were, although they may not have realised it, merely the latest in a long line of rebels. By comparison the efforts of their predecessors might have appeared very tame, but it took just as much courage to flout the strict etiquette of the 1920s and 1930s (which required nurses to remain seated in the dining room until released by Matron) by creeping out through the door on hands and knees for a quick smoke – only the *most* unlucky crawled into the Assistant Matron or Home Sister on the way!

There was also disenchantment with the old order in the school of nursing. Like their colleagues in other schools, the tutors were dissatisfied with their relatively lowly status in the nursing hierarchy (in some hospitals the tutors were better qualified than their matrons) and with a system which gave them little real responsibility. Feelings ran high, and at one point Matron, who had given the school virtual independence, had to intervene to calm the waters. Miss Mitchell resigned as Principal Tutor in 1963 to work overseas for the World Heath Organisation. Under her direction the work of the school had greatly expanded and the number of tutors had been increased from three to seven. Nurses at all levels of training now spent much more time there, and in-service classes for trained staff had been started. Miss Mitchell had also created closer understanding with students in other disciplines by giving lectures to physiotherapists, radiographers, and medical students.[8]

She was succeeded by Miss A.P.I. Logan who was one of two Royal-trained tutors (the other, Miss P.A.Irvine, was also on the school staff) to take part in an exchange of tutors between Northern Ireland, Canada and the United States.[9] The visiting tutors reported on their findings and made recommendations which were published in an Exchange Report.[10] Suggestions for improvements in the Royal included a closer liaison between school and wards, greater student status for nurses and the delegation of more responsibility by the Principal Tutor to her staff. With these in mind, a new three-year training course was devised. For the first time the subjects studied in the classroom were followed by periods of practical experience in the

It's easier to read when its typed. Miss Logan, the Principal Tutor, and nurses in the school library. (Nursing Mirror, London)

same area. For example, lectures in surgery and surgical nursing were followed by a period of practical work in a surgical ward. It also ensured that nurses who were sent for basic nursing experience to a specialty such as neurosurgery or cardiology, returned for further experience at a more senior level. No longer was the compulsory period in 'gynae', for example, finished before a nurse had been taught any gynaecology. The course included psychiatry and (at long last!) paediatric nursing, with practical experience in Purdysburn Hospital and in the RBHSC or the Ulster Hospital. (The unaccustomed contact with infectious diseases in the children's hospitals unfortunately meant that a period of paediatric experience was often followed by a period of sick leave!) Community nursing was also added to the new curriculum and the preliminary state examination was replaced by a ward-based assessment. An important feature of the new programme was that each student knew her entire course, including holiday periods, in advance.

Internal rotation gave continuity of experience as well as care. It was already the practice for some nurses to get their theatre experience on night duty, a system that had its drawbacks, as most night operations were emergencies and not usually performed by the consultants. One junior on theatre night duty was so overawed by the unexpected arrival of the Professor of Surgery in the middle of the night that, hearing the great man say, 'Mop, please' – a request to have the perspiration wiped from his brow – dashed helpfully into the ward to fetch the bucket and floor mop! This hazard was now removed.

Although full student status, long sought by reformers of nurse training, was not yet possible, an effort was made to meet this Exchange Report recommendation by extending the time allocated to classroom work to twenty-six weeks and allowing the nurses on block study to wear mufti. They were also allowed to live out when attending the school in their final year.

The Report had also suggested that more should be done to help nurses understand the confusing world of the hospital, and to give them support, particularly in their first encounters with serious illness and death. So, at the start of each training course, the new student nurses were now given a talk on the administration of the hospital and taken on a conducted tour of the premises. Each group was also allocated an assistant matron or home sister who would act as their mentor, and whom they could consult about any problems which occurred whilst they were in training. When the new programme started in January 1965, Miss McCullough, who was in charge of nurse allocations, compiled friendship lists to ensure that, as far as possible, friends had compatible duty rosters. The support of friends was, and always has been, very important if difficult times are to be endured – and every nurse in training has some difficult times.

In order to ensure the smooth running of the new scheme, and to avoid switching nurses from ward to ward to meet unexpected emergencies as had been done in the past, a team of relief nurses was maintained – the equivalent of a full ward staff – and allocated as necessary by Miss McCullough.

When the new restaurant in Bostock House was opened, the kitchens and dining room were no longer needed in Musson House, so the school was able to expand. The Beeches also became redundant and was closed at the end of 1964.

Enrolled nurse training had been established in a number of other hospitals for some years, but it was not available in the Royal until 1964, when a school was opened at the Throne Hospital, with Mrs Collier in charge. Pupil nurses, distinguished by green uniforms and different badges, obtained part of their practical experience in the Royal. In 1973 this educational outpost was also amalgamated with the main school.

A new experimental course of training for dual qualification in psychiatric and and general nursing was started in 1965 in conjunction with Purdysburn Hospital. Mr J.A.Ferguson, a tutor with psychiatric training and experience, and the first man to be appointed to the school staff, was put in charge. Nurses undertaking the course also wore different badges and a distinctive grey uniform – which earned them the nickname of Grey Girls.

Tired of the extraordinary variations which had developed in the original VAD caps of the 1920s, Miss Elliott asked the student nurses themselves to devise a new style. The version chosen was based on one used in the Erne Hospital in Enniskillen, the butterfly wing cap in use today.[11] The prospective nurse who, while waiting outside Matron's office for interview in the 1940s, had likened the group of young nurses which erupted through the doors of West Wing to a flock of birds, would have seen an even greater similarity twenty years later.

While all kinds of innovations were being welcomed, there were also some nostalgic farewells. One of the first in a series of notable retirements was Maggie Cranston (Big Maggie), wardsmaid in Wards 11 and 12 for over thirty years, her formidable figure and personality indelibly engraved in the memory of everyone who knew her. One ex-patient described her as, 'better than most nurses at making a patient comfortable in bed, and better than any at making an egg nogg'. When Professor Rodgers demanded of Matron that the over-

bearing Maggie should be removed from his ward, he must have been surprised, to say the least, to be told, half seriously, 'It would take an Act of Parliament to do that'. The Brig (the former Medical Superintendent) retired in 1965, but for nurses the most momentous departures were in the summer of 1966 when Matron, Miss F.E. Elliott; the Deputy Matron, Miss Nora Earls; and Assistant Matron, Miss Mary Scott, left within a few weeks of each other. It seemed to many to be the end of an era – and in a way it was.

Miss Elliott was awarded an OBE in 1951 for her services to nursing and in 1967 this work was further recognised by the unprecedented award (to a nurse) of an honorary Master of Arts degree from The Queen's University of Belfast. Retirement in Australia has given time and opportunity for a host of new interests, but she has maintained close links with the hospital, and has been the guiding spirit behind the establishment of an Australian branch of the RVH League of Nurses. Her home is an essential stopping off point for any member of the Royal staff – past or present – visiting Melbourne, where one consultant found to his surprise that Miss Elliott knew more than he did of what was happening in the hospital – where he was still working! More than two decades after her retirement her advice is still sought – and taken – by many of her former nurses, now a worldwide 'family'. An annual lecture in her honour was inaugurated in 1982.

In the twenty years of her stewardship, the Health Service was firmly established, and the hospital's finances were put on a secure footing. Nurses' hours were reduced and their pay increased. They were relieved of much of their domestic work, and routines were revised and rationalised. The comfort of patients had also been improved and greater consideration given to the welfare of their relatives and friends. A second level of nurse training had been established, and new courses introduced. Doctors and nurses who came to the Royal from other hospitals, to visit or to work, found its standards to be equal to the best in the United Kingdom. In the following decades the hospital's specialist expertise was to become world famous, but for reasons which brought more sadness than pride. One of the unique features of Miss Elliott's period in office was that she was the only Matron of the hospital in the twentieth century whose work was not disrupted by serious conflict – international war or the civil disturbances so euphemistically known in Ireland as the Troubles.

8   Into Troubled Waters   1966 – 1973

In the late 1960s the bed shortage had reached crisis point. Wards began their stint of emergency take-in duty with every bed already full and with patients on transfer to other parts of the hospital. The 1969 influenza epidemic swamped the general medical wards, and the Gynaecology, Ophthalmic and Metabolic wards had to be emptied in turn to admit influenza patients.

So, in spite of the earlier decision not to build anew on the site, plans were made to build a new 150-bedded block. As a first step, a link block was built to join the new building to the main hospital. This provided room for a general intensive care unit and better accommodation for the Respiratory Failure Unit.

Even in the nineteenth century, the 'clogging' of beds by long-term elderly patients had been a problem; with an ageing population the problem increased. Partly to relieve beds in the main wards for acute cases, but also to provide a better service for geriatric patients, a seventy-two bed geriatric unit was opened in 1971. It was named Florence Elliott House after the former Matron. Because of a staffing shortage – geriatrics tends to be the Cinderella of the Health Service – it was only possible to open the new unit in stages. Later, to conserve staff, an experimental five-day system was introduced, with patients spending the weekends at home. This was so popular with both patients and staff that it was made a regular feature.

Meanwhile, internal re-organisation continued as before to provide for other growing specialties. The insatiable Cardiology Department infiltrated the first floor of West Wing, and later acquired part of Extern as well. Its surgical counterpart was allocated Wards 13 and 14 as a chest and heart surgery unit – now needed more than ever with the increase in open heart surgery. (This had begun in the Royal in 1967, with coronary bypass surgery added in 1969.)

The most spectacular new addition, however was the magnificent nine storey Outpatient Centre where, for the first time since the early years of the century, all casualty and outpatient services were housed under one roof. It included an observation ward with a full nursing staff – a far cry from the ex-army hut, one nurse, and Tilly.

The complex process of equipping the Outpatient Centre, and transferring the scattered clinics and departments to their new home was organised by a team which included an assistant matron, Miss M.A.Galbraith (a sister of the Theatre Superintendent), who remained in charge of nursing in the Centre when it opened.[1] The first patients were accepted in February 1969.[2]

In comparison with the old Extern, the new surroundings were palatial – as one patient remarked, 'It's better than Aldergrove Airport'! It took fifty Pink Ladies to help guide the patients through the bewildering maze of floors and corridors. But the work continued as before. Casualty in the Royal was, and still is, regarded as a neighbourhood first aid centre, and even today the regulars, many of them alcoholics, still wait for attention on its seats. It is almost certain that the concern of the local people for 'their' hospital was what saved it a few years later when threats to bomb it were not carried out.

The new Casualty Department was given a baptism of fire when, a few months after opening, serious rioting close to the hospital brought

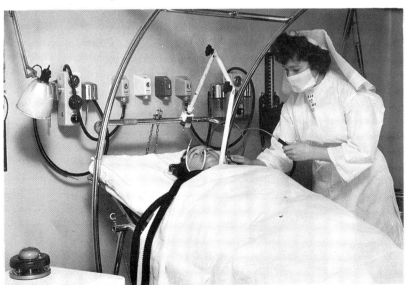

Nurse in Intensive Care Unit (c.1973.)
(RVH, Belfast)

the first victims of the current Troubles through its doors. The rioting virtually cut the hospital off from the outside world so, when the situation appeared ominous, arrangements were made to ensure that there would always be enough senior nurses on the site throughout the night. Matron was always on call. Beds were put up in every available space in West Wing, where non-resident staff could sleep if they were not immediately needed, or if it was considered unsafe for them to venture home. If the coast seemed to be clear and if they were not needed, they were sent home by taxi.

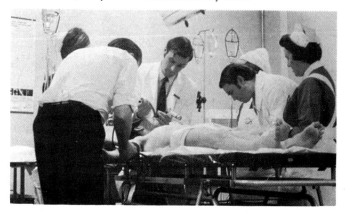

Another casualty. Sister Kate O'Hanlon keeps a watchful eye on the doctors. (Nursing Mirror, London)

The nurse administrator first on the scene – often Miss Betty or Miss McFarland, who lived on site – checked that there were enough nurses available to cover Casualty, theatres, Intensive Care Unit and take-in wards, and then saw to it that the workers themselves were looked after. Sandwiches were brought to those whose work prevented them from getting to the canteen. Concern for the well-being of the staff in these stressful times continued into the following days, when care was taken to ensure that those who had been under greatest pressure got adequate off-duty and suitably qualified relief.

Later, when the focus of the disturbances moved away from the hospital, off-duty members of staff, doctors and nurses came in as soon as they heard of an incident – either because they had heard a bomb explode or the news of one on the radio. It was not uncommon for doctors and nurses in key areas to be either en route to, or already at, their posts before the official police alert was received.

Many other people offered to help. Student nurses volunteered for extra duty; former nurses telephoned to ask what they could do; staff from the School of Nursing bridged the gap between day and night staff when their arrival was delayed by barricades, bombs or bullets. Welcome assistance also came from medical students, medical social workers, chaplains, ancillary and voluntary staff. When the Army established its field ambulance unit in Extern, its personnel helped in the hospital when not needed on the streets. Several nurses from England and Scotland spent their holidays working voluntarily in the Royal. Help also came from community nurses and hospitals in quieter areas of the Province.

Letters of appreciation and praise for the work of the hospital flooded in during the early years of the Troubles. Many distinguished visitors, including two Archbishops of Canterbury, came to deliver their messages in person. Two decades later, it is taken for granted that the Royal will cope – as it always has.

As a result of their experience in dealing with the victims of urban guerrilla warfare, some members of the medical and nursing staff of the Royal have become internationally recognised experts in this field.[3] Observers have come from many parts of the world to study its emergency system and surgical techniques. Staff have also been invited to lecture throughout the United Kingdom and abroad. Sister Kate O'Hanlon (Sister in charge of the Casualty department) travelled to New Zealand in 1981 to speak at the Australasian Critical Care Nurses Annual Conference – the first non-American nurse to be given this honour.

In acknowledgement of the nurses' role in the care and treatment of casualties in the early years of the Troubles Sister O'Hanlon and Sister A.N.Gibson (RICU) received MBEs in the 1973 Queen's Birthday Honours and Matron, Miss M.K.Robb, was awarded an OBE.

It was just as well that Miss Robb could not see what lay ahead of her when she took office in 1966. Only her first two years as Matron would be peaceful – though not without problems. It was largely her courage and devotion to duty which carried her through five further traumatic years.

Kathleen Robb started her career on the Falls Road where she qualified as a sick children's nurse in the RBHSC, moving from there to the Royal. General training was followed by orthopaedic nursing at the Robert Jones and Agnes Hunt Orthopaedic Hospital in Oswestry, Shropshire, before she returned as a sister to the Fracture and Orthopaedic Clinic. Midwifery training and a nursing administration course preceeded her appointment as Matron of the City and Tower Hill Hospitals, Armagh, from where she came back to the Royal as Nurse Planning Officer.

Miss McFarland was promoted to become her Deputy Matron, and two new assistant matrons, Miss F.K Betty and Miss A.W.Patton completed her staff.

*The last Matron, Miss
M.K.Robb, 1966-73.
(RVH, Belfast)*

The Troubles tested Royal nurses as they had never been tested before. Dealing with the victims of violence was by no means a new experience for them – many disasters had been coped with over the years; nor was the element of personal risk unknown – although the hospital had received no direct hits in 1941, the danger had been there; and there had been rioting close to the hospital in earlier Troubles; but never before had the disruption continued for so long.

While the excitement of dealing with a major emergency can overcome tiredness to a certain extent, it is much more difficult to keep going the next day and the next, when sleep is broken by the sound of bombs or gunfire (sometimes so close that, to avoid ricochetting bullets, nurses had to sleep under their beds instead of in them) and work is disrupted and nerves set on edge by frequent bomb scares. To the amazement of their seniors some junior nurses, by plugging their ears with cotton wool, managed to sleep through even the noisiest nights.

Gunfire, unfortunately, was not restricted to the world outside. One day when Matron was busy in her office she heard what sounded like a shot. On investigation she found that an attempted armed robbery of the bank in the hospital had been foiled by a security guard, and that the gunman had been shot and mortally wounded. By exercising her uniformed authority to the full, she was able to prevent an already very nasty situation from becoming worse.

An official thank-you. Sister Dessa Dodds (Neurosurgical Unit) meets the Prime Minister, Mr Heath, at a reception for 'front line' workers at Stormont. (Belfast Newsletter)

For those living on site there was *usually* no problem in getting to and from work, but the non residents often had great difficulty when there was violence in the vicinity of the hospital. Even when all appeared to be quiet, there was always the feeling that they might be in the line of fire of a hidden sniper as they passed through dark and silent streets; or that their car might be hijacked. Many of those who

were dependent on public transport, including Miss Gaw the Night Superintendent, often had to walk miles to get on duty. Others were brought in cars by friends or relatives, who then had to face another frightening journey home.

In addition, a worrying shortage of trained nurses developed, primarily because people were reluctant to work in the area but also because of Health Service economies. As well as the Geriatric Unit, the stressful Neurosurgical and Intensive Care Units had problems keeping staff. Student nurses could not really be used to make up numbers in these units because of the high level of skill required.

Enormous efforts were made to increase the recruitment of trained nurses and to lessen the drop out rate. A Back to Nursing campaign was launched to encourage even more former Royal nurses to come back to work, and a crèche was set up for the mothers of young children. More part-timers were employed. The rule which required student nurses to stop training upon marriage was relaxed, and married student nurses were allowed to live out.[4]

Youth and energy were vital as the pace of life in the Royal accelerated and the stress of the civil disturbances took its toll. It must have been with a certain sense of relief that several of its senior members finished their working careers. Into retirement in 1968 went Sister Benson (Benny) and four other popular members of staff – Miss E.L. Duff, the diminutive Assistant Matron; Miss Jean Dickson, Warden of Bostock House (and her equally popular twin sister Belle, the Senior Radiographer); and Sisters Pearn and McMath. The latter two had seen the specialty of cardiology grow from birth to maturity in the hospital. Two assistant matrons also left, Miss McCullough to become Matron of the Lurgan and Portadown Hospital and Miss Patton to take up a post as Nursing Supervisor in the Toronto Western Hospital in Canada. To replace them and Miss Duff came Miss M.B. Kerr, who had been appointed as a second night superintendent in 1966, Miss A.R. McCullough and Miss E.A. Edwards. In 1970 the Theatre Superintendent, Miss C.McQ. Galbraith left to become Matron of The Princess Elizabeth Hospital, Guernsey, and was replaced by her deputy Miss A. Grant.

It is perhaps too easy to over-emphasise the impact of the Troubles. Most of the time, the daily routine continued as normal. Sisters were more concerned about how to find room for yet another patient in their overcrowded wards, and student nurses about losing contact with friends through illness or night duty, than either were about yet another bomb. To a certain extent, familiarity was breeding contempt. Gun battles between the Army and the IRA in the vicinity of the Tower

Soldiers? Where?
Nurses pass Army post
on their way to work
(c.1970). (Nursing
Mirror, London)

blocks (An Army observation post had been established on the roof of one) became so routine that Miss Robb had to ask the PTS leaders to warn their colleagues of the danger of watching these battles from the balconies of their flats! One nurse, leaving the Towers with her boy-friend, had to crouch for several minutes beside his car to avoid ricochetting bullets – but continued with her evening out when the shooting temporarily ceased.

It is ironic that one of the most universally disruptive events of these years, the Ulster Workers' Strike of 1974, left the hospital rela-tively unscathed. Some ancillary workers were intimidated and afraid to come in to work, but it was possible to carry on much of the normal routine with the aid of the emergency generator when the rest of the country was having massive power cuts.

However casually the nurses appeared to take the Troubles, they were undoubtedly under considerable stress, and often in danger as well when going to or from the hospital. To help reduce the need to go out for entertainment, and to boost morale, more on-site recreation was provided. Film shows, discos and facilities for playing bridge were organised; a bowling green, laid down behind the Geriatric Unit, was ready for use in 1972. A shop was opened in the Towers. In 1970, a recreation room and coffee bar were provided in the basement of Musson House. The RVH Working-men's Committee provided a ste-reo record player and the Army unit then stationed on the site gave a selection of records. (This was not the only time the Army helped the nurses. In the autumn of 1971 flooding cut off access to the Towers. Willing soldiers carried nurses across the flood-water. When Matron later went to thank them, they said, 'Ma'am – it was a pleasure!')

As far as possible other off duty interests were kept up too. The nurses' squash team won the Silver Plate in the 'B' League in 1968-69. The choir, which had expanded to include physiotherapists, radiographers and other ancillary staff as well as nurses and doctors, continued to give periodic concerts. The Nurses Christian Fellowship, which now also welcomed other staff, amalgamated with its counterpart in the RBHSC, and the Student Nurses Association continued to be active.

Because of the difficulty in getting on and off the site and the disruption of public transport, the management organised a regular bus service to and from the City Hall. In 1973, one of the worst years, a minibus also ferried nurses between the Towers and work. Their isolation on the periphery of the site was emphasised during the first night of rioting in the area, when they were completely cut off from the rest of the hospital. When Miss Robb, the first outsider on the scene next morning, arrived to check that everyone was all right, she saw faces looking down at her from every window and remarked that she felt like the US Cavalry riding to the relief of a beleaguered garrison!

Growing specialisation and the complexity of many of the new treatments increased the need for in-service training in the school and, for the first time, short postgraduate courses were organised for recognised qualifications in ear, nose and throat, theatre and intensive care nursing. A shortened eighteen-month course for registered sick children's nurses from the RBHSC to qualify as SRNs, was also started in 1969.

After long and often acrimonious discussions, the Nurses and Midwives (N.I.) Act was passed in 1971, which led to major changes in the structure of nurse training in Northern Ireland. A new statutory body, the Northern Ireland Council for Nurses and Midwives (N.I.Council), replaced the Joint Council on January 1, 1971. In addition to the former duties of the Joint Council, the new body assumed full responsibility for all nurse training, basic and post-basic, including the employment of staff. Although the school in the Royal had been independent in all but name for some time, now, after almost seventy years, responsibility for nurse training was once more officially – and legally – separated from the hospital administration.

Until the extensive changes planned by the new Council were put into effect, the existing training scheme continued, but not without problems. It was becoming increasingly difficult to provide sufficient basic nursing experience for student nurses as specialisation within the hospital increased. However, they continued to be allocated to

Opposite: Changing headgear. A century of nursing millinery at the Royal.

Changing headgear

Joan O'Neill

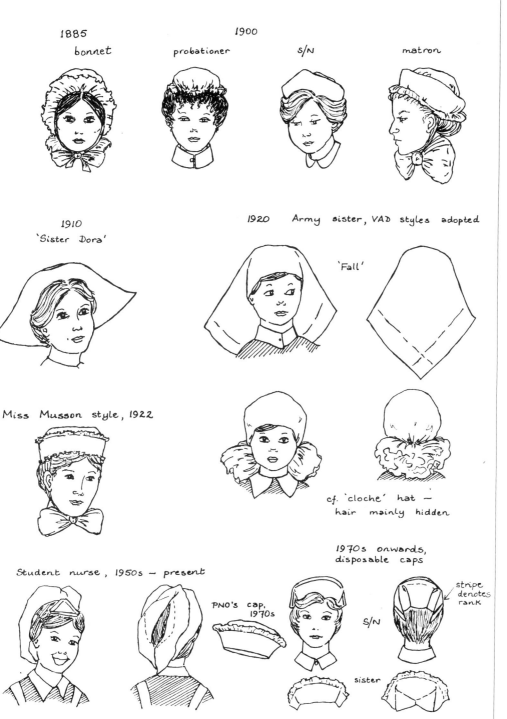

1885
bonnet

1900
probationer   S/N   matron

1910
'Sister Dora'

1920   Army sister, VAD styles adopted

'Fall'

Miss Musson style, 1922

cf. 'cloche' hat —
hair mainly hidden

1970s onwards,
disposable caps

Student nurse, 1950s – present

PNO's cap,
1970s

S/N

stripe
denotes
rank

sister

Fall remains for S/Ns and sisters until '70s

specialist departments in spite of some opposition by the N.I.Council, which felt that these were unsuitable for basic training. Matron and the Principal Tutor disagreed, both of them believing that basic nursing was an integral part of the care of all patients.

The school, like most others in the country, was short of qualified tutors, particularly since the increase of in-service training. To help ease the problem, some classes were amalgamated with the RBHSC, and in 1971 clinical instructors, a new grade in the nurse tutor hierarchy, were added to the staff. Although the shortage of tutors often meant them helping in the classroom, their main function was bedside teaching.

It was not only the school that underwent radical changes. There were two major administrative reforms in the Health Service in Northern Ireland in late 1973. The first was the introduction of a system of line management into the nursing administration – the result of recommendations made by the Salmon Committee in 1966.[5] The main purpose was to improve career prospects within the service and, by clarifying the roles of the different administrative grades, to raise the level of job satisfaction. It had already been implemented in England and Wales, but was delayed in Northern Ireland because of the impending Health Service reorganisation. Preparations for it started nevertheless, and senior members of staff, including Matron, were sent on management training courses run by the Royal College of Nursing. Meantime, in October 1973, a complete reorganisation of local government and the health and social services took place.

The Hospitals Authority and the County Health Committees were replaced by four area health boards, which brought all their hospital and community health and social services under a single administrative umbrella for the first time. The areas were sub-divided into districts, the Royal being included in the North and West Belfast District of the Eastern Health and Social Services Board.

Miss Robb relinquished her position as Matron to become District Administrative Nursing Officer for North and West Belfast. While her new post distanced her from the day to day work of the Royal (the District included the Mater Infirmorum and Claremont Street Hospitals as well as the three hospitals on the Royal site and the community nursing services), she retained close links both in her new post and through her association with the Nurses League, of which she was Acting and later Joint President.

One of Matron's other hats. Dressed for a topping off ceremony c.1970. (Miss M.K. Robb, Dundonald)

Like her predecessors she devoted great effort and energy to nursing affairs outside the hospital. She was a member both of the National Council and the N.I.Board of the Royal College of Nursing, serving as

Chairman of the latter from 1969-72 and 1976-77. She also served on the Nursing and Midwifery Services Committee of the Hospitals Authority and the Standing Nursing and Midwifery Advisory Committee to the Department of Health and Social Services. She was appointed a Fellow of the Royal College of Nursing in 1977, a year after the Fellowships were first introduced.

Miss Robb handed over to her successor after just seven years in office, She was the last to be officially called Matron, although there was still to be a head of nursing in the hospital for another decade. If her stay was short, it was also eventful, and not only because of the Troubles – they just made it more difficult. Although her predecessor, Miss Elliott, had been the first Matron to attend Management Committee meetings, she had been admitted not as head of nursing in the hospital but as Chairman of the Group Matrons' Committee and later of the Group Nursing Advisory Committee. The appointment of Miss Robb as Nurse Planning Officer – the first in any major teaching hospital in the United Kingdom – had pushed the door of nurse representation at the highest levels open a little further. It was during her time as Matron, however, that it became fully accepted – albeit reluctantly by some – that nurses should be represented at every level of administration where nursing matters were involved. When the hospital advisory committees were replaced by a 'Cogwheel' structure (with a core committee made up of the chairmen of the individual sectors), Matron, as representative of the nursing services section, was an undisputed member. The inclusion of nurses at top level in the new health services structure as Chief Area Nursing Officer and District Administrative Nursing Officer – posts not envisaged in the original plan[6] – owes much to the efforts of the Northern Ireland Committee of the Royal College of Nursing, of which Miss Robb was Chairman.

9 Under New Management 1973 – 1975

One of Miss Robb's first tasks as District Administrative Nursing Officer (DANO) was to implement the Salmon Committee's recommendations in the Royal. In earlier discussions a major issue had been whether or not there should still be a matron-figure (by whatever name) at the head of nursing in the hospital. It was agreed that there should. In December 1973 Miss M.A. McFarland, Miss Robb's former Deputy Matron who had been Acting Matron since her departure, became the hospital's first Principal Nursing Officer (PNO). The choice was a happy one. Change was coming, and the presence at the head of nursing of a familiar, popular and capable figure undoubtedly helped ensure continuity at a time of when the familiar structures of the Belfast Hospitals Management Committee were being replaced. Miss McFarland's period in office was the shortest of all the Matrons, but because it was also a time of interesting changes it merits a chapter to itself.

The Salmon Committee had divided the nursing hierarchy into ten grades, and changed the titles where necessary to accommodate the growing number of men in nursing. (The only 'sexist' title to be retained was sister – the male equivalent being charge nurse.) All had approximate equivalents already on the Royal staff, with the exception of Grade 10 which was similar to the former post of group matron. Under the new system the old pattern of direct liaison between matron and ward sister was changed to a system of line management with each level from ward sister upwards responsible to the level above. This was not unlike the pattern that already operated within the ward staff, so it was only at senior level that reorganisation was needed.

Next in line to the PNO (Salmon 9) were the senior nursing officers (SNO - Salmon 8). Most of those appointed in December 1973 were already assistant matrons, night or theatre superintendents. Only those whose new duties were to be substantially different from their previous work had to reapply. The others were simply assimilated and given new titles. Each senior nursing officer was given a specific area of work to oversee. Between the senior nursing officers and the ward sisters was inserted the new grade of nursing officer (NO), without doubt the most controversial part of the Salmon system in the Royal. At the beginning, however, there was little or no difficulty as almost all the first nursing officers appointed were already departmental sisters or assistant matrons – posts with a predominantly managerial role. Initially only two completely new posts were created in this grade, one for cardiology and the other for the surgical wards. Fourteen nursing officers in all were appointed.

In later years problems arose as the number of nursing officers proliferated. By 1982 the total had risen to twenty-two. Although it was a management rather than a clinical grade, some of the ward sisters saw the nursing officer as a threat to their own status. The situation was even more unacceptable if the nursing officer, who was on a higher pay scale, was unfamiliar with the ward sister's particular specialty. In spite of these difficulties, many ward sisters chose to remain in clinical work, preferring the direct contact with patients to management. Others, unwilling to be subordinate to a nursing officer, or interested in moving into the managerial side of nursing, applied for the posts and were appointed as nursing officers themselves. Consultants who lost experienced ward sisters to the new management structure were dissatisfied – and said so – which did not make the work of the new nursing officers any easier. More than one nursing officer later abandoned her newly acquired navy dress (both nursing officers and senior nursing officers wore the same uniform as the former assistant matrons) to return to clinical work and a red dress; one even found administrative work so unsatisfying that she accepted a sister's post at a lower grade than she had previously held. There were, and are, good as well as not so good nursing officers, but they have had an uphill struggle to gain acceptance.

One of the greatest changes brought about by the new structure was the loss of direct contact between the ward sister and the head of nursing. Previously, when she had a problem, a ward sister had been able to go directly to Matron for advice. Now she had to speak first to her Nursing Officer; who, if she was unable to offer a solution, passed the problem on to the Senior Nursing Officer; and only if she had not the necessary authority might the Principal Nursing Officer consulted. From the ward sister's point of view, this system did not have a great deal to recommend it, but the sheer size of the hospital has made it impossible for the head of nursing to be involved with every problem. Delegation was essential.

For the senior nursing officer who had formerly been an assistant matron, the new structure was an improvement. Previously she had been what her title implied, an assistant to Matron, and as such was obliged to do as Matron required. While her duties usually were in keeping with her rank and experience, they could also be extremely trivial and frustrating. More than one assistant matron, as she stood checking piles of nurses' aprons to see if they required mending, or interrupted the work of a busy ward to check the number of rubber mattresses on its beds, wondered if her talents might have been more usefully employed if she had remained in clinical nursing. Now they acquired a clearly defined role.

Although at first not slotted into the Salmon structure, an important new addition to the nursing staff in 1974, was a stoma care nurse, Sister J.McH. Roberts. Her work as a stomatherapist included teaching and research as well as pre and post-operative counselling and advice to stoma patients, and her contribution to the physical and psychological wellbeing of these patients was invaluable. In 1979 the post was upgraded to that of nursing officer. Subsequently, however, the authorities decided that the Stomatherapist should spend more time on administration. Miss Roberts found this arrangement unsatisfactory and she resigned to work as a stomatherapist in the private sector. It was some time before a permanent replacement could be found.

The appointment of a specialist nurse stomatherapist was a significant advance for the nursing profession, whose expertise has traditionally been inherited from the medical profession rather than being of its own making.[1]

The second major administrative change was in the school. By 1974 the N.I. Council had completed its plans for the reorganisation of nurse training in the Province. In June, the RVH school finally ceased to exist. It's successor was the Belfast Northern Group School of Nursing which combined the schools of the RVH, the RBHSC and the Mater Infirmorum Hospital. The first Principal Administrative Education Officer (PAEO) to take charge of the new school was the former tutor, Mr J.A. Ferguson. Mrs Ritchie was made responsible for all basic training courses and Sister M. Genevieve of the Mater School for post basic training. One tutor acted as a liaison officer with the hospitals where the nurses would go for practical experience. Only the selection

Miss M.A. McFarland, Principal Nursing Officer 1973-75. The first of the post-matron matrons. (RVH, Belfast)

of candidates for training remained the responsibility of the hospitals.

The new school was based in Musson House where, to make room for the extra students, the sitting room was taken over as a library and a temporary classroom was erected in the grounds. Some time later several rooms in Bostock House were also given to the school.

Not only was the new PAEO a man, but men were making their presence felt in other areas of nursing in the hospital. There had been male charge nurses in the Special (Venereology) Clinic for some time, and in 1972 Mr W.J. Carville was appointed to the night staff as charge nurse and later promoted to nursing officer. The first male chairman of the RVH Student Nurses Association Unit, Mr F.A. Rice, was elected in 1969, and in 1975 Mr H.A. Reid became the first male nurse to be awarded the gold medal – in International Women's Year!

The staffing problem just would not go away. Not only was the continuing civil unrest still affecting the recruitment and retention of staff but, after a long period without any shortage of applicants for training, parents were becoming increasingly reluctant to allow their daughters to go to such a high risk area. Trained nurses were coaxed from wherever they could be found. One even travelled from Omagh each week to do two consecutive nights on night duty, sleeping in Bostock House during the intervening day. Permission was obtained from the N.I. Council to allow nurses who had previously dropped out from training to complete their course – the Council deciding how much time each one needed to do. These more mature students were found to make excellent members of staff once they settled in.

There was also difficulty with accommodation. For some time, student nurses as well as trained staff had been allowed to live out, and the demand for rooms or flats on the site had dwindled. But the Troubles brought many of the non-residents hurrying back – in the case of one group of four student nurses, precipitately so. The four shared a rented house in Broadway. On returning home from lectures one evening they found strangers moving into their house, supervised by four strong men who were standing on the other side of the street, looking anything but friendly. The girls were allowed into the house to collect their belongings, which they did with all possible haste and, very frightened, arrived at the Nursing Administration Office to appeal for help. After that, living out in the neighbourhood of the hospital became noticably less popular. Rooms were found in the Musgrave and Clark Clinic for nurses who felt it was safer inside the walls.

Violence continued inside as well as outside the hospital. Following a shooting incident in the Maze prison, when some of the prisoners were brought in for treatment, Miss McFarland was called urgently to Casualty to find that a belligerent mob of friends and relatives had taken possession of the waiting area. Realising the urgent need to prevent an invasion of the treatment area, she placed herself strategically between the crowd and the treatment rooms and, accompanied by an administrator and a priest, managed to contain the crowd in the waiting area. (It was not what one imagines Florence Nightingale envisaged her matrons doing, but one cannot help thinking that Miss Nightingale would have approved of Miss McFarland's courage and prompt action.)

Violence, though generally on a smaller scale, was a feature of Casualty. Nurses working there in recent years have become almost inured to aggression from patients, and their relatives or friends, particularly at night. Bruises and bumps received in the course of duty have become so common as to be accepted as part and parcel of casualty work.

Although her official title was Principal Nursing Officer, Miss McFarland was still regarded by most as Matron – and called it by some. Outwardly her role appeared to be little different from that of her predecessors. Like them she continued to do a round of part of the buildings each day and was seen, as well as known, to be the head of nursing in the hospital. But the old order was changing, and under her successor, Miss Heather Barratt, the changes would soon become apparent.

10   Shortages, Strikes and Shootings 1975 – 1984

In August 1975 the first patients were admitted to Block A (Wards 37 - 44), the building intended as the first of a new hospital complex, until fate and the Exchequer had decreed otherwise. The new premises provided six theatre suites with recovery accommodation for neurosurgery, orthopaedic, fracture, accident and emergency and general surgery. It had an observation ward with twenty beds and spaces for ten night admissions; two neurosurgery wards; a burns unit; two fracture and trauma wards; topped by a floor of single rooms, the Heron Clinic, provided by a generous bequest.

While the patients found the modern ward layout – six-bedded bays and single rooms with a central administration and treatment area – pleasantly quiet, there was one major disadvantage. Supervision of high dependency patients was much more difficult than in the Nightingale wards on the main corridor. Indeed, on one occasion, the resuscitation team from the Cardiac Unit was in action in one neurosurgical ward before the sister on duty, who was busy in the other one, was aware that it had been called! The problem was resolved by dividing the Neurosurgery and the Trauma Units into two separate wards and appointing a senior and junior sister to each. Miss A.R.McCullough, who had helped commission the new building was put in charge when it opened.

Because of recruitment difficulties and shortage of nursing accommodation, the new block was brought into use in stages. The Burns Unit opened last, in 1979 (the same year as Grosvenor Tower, the third block of flats). Patients were transferred to it from the Ulster Hospital, and the Unit became the regional centre for the treatment of severe burns.

As patients and work were transferred to Block A, other uses were found for the empty spaces. The Observation Ward in the Outpatient Block was used for patients recovering from day surgery; Ward 21 was given over to neurology and dental patients and Ward 22 to rheumatology, haematology and later to gastroenterology; Wards 17 and 18 were converted to general and vascular surgery; and Wards 9 and 10 made into a medical unit to relieve the pressure on this section of the hospital. Private patients and overflow cardiology patients were transferred to the Heron Clinic from the Musgrave and Clark Clinic, which was then given to the resident medical staff and renamed Musgrave and Clark House. There was a nostalgic moment when the last housemen left East Wing for their new home.

In 1979 a new wing and day clinic were added to Florence Elliott House and named Catherine Dynes House after the former Night

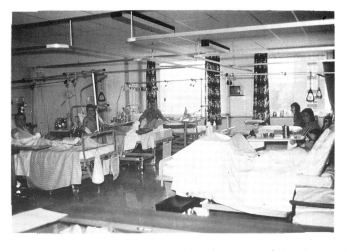

Farewell Nightingale.
The new-style wards
in Block A.
(RVH, Belfast)

Superintendent. It is ironic that the part of the hospital chosen to honour two of its most illustrious nurses should be the Geriatric Unit, as anyone less like the popular image of the geriatric than these two ladies in later years would be difficult to imagine. What is reflected, however, is their life-long concern for the sick or infirm of any age.

Not surprisingly, cardiology was looking for yet more space. Wards 7 and 8 were divided, and Ward 7 was added to the Coronary Care Unit in 5 and 6. Ward 8 remained a general medical unit. Each ward was made 'unisex' – a change that must have made the hospital's Victorian forebears turn in their graves!

They would also, no doubt, have been bemused by the computers that were now finding their way into the clinical areas of the hospital.

Although some of the staff in the Cardiology unit (where the first of these was installed), had completed their schooling in the pre-computer era, and contemplated the arrival of this new wizardry with some trepidation, they soon mastered its mysteries.

Computer studies, however, were not yet included in nurse training, which was again in a state of flux following the publication of the EEC Directive on Nursing in 1977. This required everyone undertaking general nurse training from June 1979 to have experience in obstetric, psychiatric, geriatric, paediatric and community nursing as well as the traditional core subjects. The curriculum in the school had to be adjusted and the opportunity was taken to introduce a new modular scheme of training at the same time. The new course (which was so precisely calculated that, when nurses hours were reduced to $37^{1}/2$ a week in 1981 it had to be extended by eight weeks) was divided into thirteen week modules, each starting with a period in the classroom, followed by related practical experience and ending with another week in the school. Experience in obstetrics (the one totally new addition to the previous training options) was given in the Royal Maternity Hospital, and each nurse also spent three weeks with a district nurse, and one with a health visitor. Each module was assessed either by ward progress reports, or a ward-based assignment and a written examination during the final week in the school.

There was another upheaval in nurse education in 1983, when training throughout the United Kingdom was coordinated for the first time.[1] The Northern Ireland Council for Nurses and Midwives was disbanded and replaced by the Northern Ireland Board of the Central Council for Training Nurses, Midwives and Health Visitors (thankfully abbreviated to UKCC!). A number of changes quickly followed. A single professional register for nurses, midwives and health visitors replaced all existing registers. A code of professional conduct was devised. Finally, State Registered Nurses were translated into Registered General Nurses (RGN) – a title long in use in Scotland.

Although at times there was still a shortage of recruits, there were usually enough to meet the hospital's needs. Trained nurses were still the problem, and Miss Heather M.C.Barratt, who succeeded Miss MacFarland as Principal Nursing Officer, relied heavily on students to fill the gaps, increasing the intake as required (just as Miss Bostock and Miss Musson had done), a practice strongly opposed by both the Area Health Board and the N.I.Council.

Miss Barratt was the sixth and final head of nursing since the Royal transferred to the Grosvenor Road. Born and educated in Kenya, she undertook her general nurse training in Bulawayo General Hospital,

Miss Heather Barratt,
Divisional Nursing
Officer, 1975-1984.
(RVH, Belfast)

returning later to Kenya to work. There, as a surgical ward sister during the Mau Mau uprisings, she had first-hand experience of guerrilla warfare and its aftermath. Later she also worked in Kenya as a provincial matron. She did her midwifery training in London and obtained a nursing administration certificate in Edinburgh. A period of work in Liverpool and another as a senior nursing officer in Leicester Royal Infirmary completed her experience before taking up her appointment in the Royal.

Once in office she took the Royal to her heart, upholding its traditions as enthusiastically as its own trainees – provided of course that maintaining tradition was compatible with a high standard of nursing. Unlike previous matrons, but in keeping with the philosophy of line management and her own inclinations, Miss Barratt was more democrat than autocrat. She consulted her nurse managers before making decisions, although she was also capable of cutting through red tape to achieve her ends. At times she became the victim of her own democratic approach, when she was criticised for not being seen in the wards, in uniform, as often as her predecessors had been. Her critics perhaps did not appreciate the work that she did behind the scenes – she was on more than a dozen committees – nor the support she gave to her administrative staff, who fully approved of her methods. Her wholehearted support of her nursing officers did not endear her to the vociferous critics of this particular grade of nurse manager. A discriminating disciplinarian, she nevertheless did not shrink from reprimanding any member of staff if she thought it necessary.

In spite of the Troubles – which did not unduly disturb her after Kenya – Miss Barratt found that not only did Royal nurses have a low sickness and absenteeism rate but that the training dropout rate was below the average for Northern Ireland and less than half that of parts of England. She attributed this to a high level of motivation amongst the student nurses, whom she also found to be pleasantly less sophisticated than their counterparts across the water. (She was also surprised, but less attracted, by the rather chauvinistic paternalism of the Ulster male!)

The proportion of men on the nursing staff remained small, but they were still making inroads at higher levels. When Mr Ferguson resigned as Principal Administrative Education Officer in 1977, he was replaced by Mr J.J. Walsh. Not until 1980, when Mrs A.P.I.Ritchie succeeded Mr Walsh, was a woman again the head of nurse training. The departure in 1979 of two Royal-trained male nurses to Scotland for midwifery training marked one more step towards the full acceptance of men into this traditionally female occupation.

If Miss Barratt was to make any progress towards solving the nursing shortage, some new way of attracting trained nurses – male and female – back to work was needed. Realising that there were many women who would like to return, but whose family commitments prevented them from undertaking regular work, she inaugurated the Nurse Bank in March 1979. It was composed of nurses who were prepared to work a minimum of eight hours a month at mutually agreeable times. A nursing officer, Miss A.Friel, organised the rotas for the Bank nurses, who telephoned her each week to say when they would be available. A one week orientation course was organised to familiarise them with new drugs, treatments and routines, as many of them had been away from nursing for some years. Most were glad to find that well-remembered routines such as bed-bathing and giving bedpans had not changed, but were not so pleased to rediscover the discomfort of sore feet after a day on duty!

The Bank proved to be very successful, and within two years had a hundred nurses available for duty. In 1980 a separate bank for nurses interested in working in the Geriatric Department was started. An extra bonus was the return of a number of Bank nurses to full-time or regular part-time work, largely because of improved crèche facilities. New post-certificate training courses also helped to increase the number of qualified nurses – albeit temporarily – in the Accident and Emergency, Neuromedical and Neurosurgical Departments.

Neither the Bank nor the new training courses were enough, however, and the shortage of trained staff remained a constant worry. The problem was not helped by the Government's determination to cut Health Service spending, and in January 1979 some staff nurses felt impelled to protest against proposed economies which, they believed, could seriously damage the Service. They also joined with medical collegues in presenting their case in the newspapers.

Keeping up the traditions. Miss Barratt, helped by Miss Betty, presents badges to newly qualified staff nurses wearing their ceremonial big caps. (Miss Anne Grant, Belfast)

But they did not strike. However, other workers on the site did, and the rest of Miss Barratt's time in office was dogged by disruptions. There was a strike of ambulance drivers in March 1978; and in July of the same year the National Union of Public Employees organised a one day strike of operating department assistants dissatisfied with new regrading and training regulations. While very inconvenient, this strike was not seriously disruptive, but the national strikes of ancillary workers – porters, domestic staff, cooks and technicians – in the following

year certainly were. There was a one day strike on 22nd January in protest at the Government's pay policies, followed by a three day strike early in February. No staff meals were cooked and the dining rooms and canteen were closed. The senior nursing and medical staff, and administrators from other disciplines and hospitals (the only workers acceptable to the unions) kept the place going, removing rubbish and soiled laundry, and delivering meals. By exercising considerable ingenuity (caution forbids details being disclosed) essential supplies were also maintained. Although the strikers had agreed to return to work if there was a major emergency, without this foresight the proper treatment of casualties in such an emergency would have been extraordinarily difficult. In March of the following year maintenance workers stopped work, and the next month another five day strike saw the medical, nursing and administrative staffs once again maintaining essential services. There were further strikes in 1982. In June cardiac surgery had to be suspended when supplies of clean linen and equipment from the GSSD were disrupted. In December a five day strike of ancillary workers interrupted heating, and laundry and sterile equipment supplies once again. As ever, the staff who remained at their posts won considerable sympathy and there were many offers of help from the public.

Violence too made the hospital newsworthy. In 1977 a porter and a soldier were assassinated on the site in separate incidents, and a

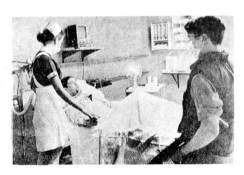

Nursing care and protection. Treating a military patient in the Intensive Care Unit. (Nursing Mirror, London)

biochemist was injured when shots were fired at the hospital bus. In 1978 an Army Saracen was ambushed in the grounds and two policemen and one soldier were injured. In 1979 a soldier guarding a patient in the Intensive Care Unit was shot and wounded. In May 1981 a gunman shot and killed a police reservist on guard duty in the same Department. Following this incident security was tightened and twelve beds were provided for security patients behind bullet-proof doors. As far as possible patients from opposing factions were kept apart but, on occasion, confrontations between relatives or between guards and relatives have occurred and nurses have had to pour oil on these troubled waters. In contrast, incongruous friendships have developed between casualties from opposite sides who found themselves in adjoining beds.

Although the staff, to a certain extent, became accustomed both to a violent environment and to dealing with the consequences of violence, nevertheless it took a special kind of courage to keep calm and to continue to care for patients when uncertain of the fate of relatives or friends who might have been caught up in a particular bombing, or when gunmen shot and killed within the hospital itself. It took even greater courage when personally threatened by one of these gunman as happened one night in 1978 to Miss Gaw, the Senior Nursing Officer on night duty, when several members of the IRA, dressed in white hospital coats, abducted one of their fellows from a sideward where he was undergoing treatment. The indomitable Miss Gaw, more concerned with the welfare of the patients disturbed by the incident than with her own safety, shrugged off the jittery gunman's threat to shoot if she moved with, 'What use would it be to shoot an

A well-deserved honour. Sister Hazel Gaw, MBE. Another Royal legend. (RVH, Belfast)

old nurse like me?' and went about her duties as if nothing untoward had happened – though inwardly petrified!

Miss Betty was another senior nursing officer to have a close call with a gunman. One day in June 1981, having completed her early morning duties, she walked out of her office just in time to see a gunman enter a ward corridor in front of her and fire a volley of shots towards the ward itself. Fortunately, neither the intended target nor anyone else was injured.

Happily, the publicity was not all bad or sad. The choice of Sister Hadessah (Dessa) Dodds from the Neurosurgical Unit as the Nurse of the Year in 1976 not only gave great pleasure to her friends and colleagues but also came as a great morale booster. Her blonde good looks, enhanced by her scarlet and white uniform, made her a favourite with photographers. She attended numerous functions and met many famous people, including the Queen. Wherever she went she was a fine advertisement for the hospital, and her award was seen by many as a tribute, not just to Dessa, but to all Royal nurses. There was more good publicity in 1978 when Miss Elizabeth M'Alister, Nursing Officer in the Surgical Area, was chosen as the *Sun* newspaper's Woman of the Year for her work in the Intensive Care Unit.

The Royal has been fortunate in having had two remarkable night superintendents, who between them held the office for seventy-two years. The second of them, Miss Hazel Gaw, retired in 1978 after twenty-eight years on night duty. She was not, however, *quite* able to emulate Sister Dynes' forty-four unbroken years because of compulsory retirement, and because she had missed *part* of one night on duty while she had a broken wrist reduced under anaesthetic. She was one of a number of long-serving senior nurses to retire in the late 1970s and early 1980s including Miss McCauley from the Eye and Ear Clinic and Miss Agnes Campbell, the SNO for the Surgical Area, none of them too sorry to leave as yet another reorganistion of the Health Service was looming.

The restructuring of the Health Boards began in 1981. It was completed in the Northern, Western and Southern Boards in the same year. However, it took two more years of prolonged and, at times, bitter and angry discussion to find an acceptable solution for the Eastern Board – or at least a solution acceptable to a majority. The preliminaries included an investigation of the work done in the Royal and, although the standard of nursing was found to be above reproach, there was criticism (among other things) of nurse management and, as ever, of the high ratio of learner to trained nurses.[2] It was suggested that an amalgamation of the three hospitals on the Royal site might be desirable.

The final plan for the area abolished the District level of management entirely, and divided the hospitals into fourteen units of management, each with a group manager directly responsible to the Area Board. The three 'Royal' hospitals formed one group with the Throne, Claremont Street and Haypark Hospitals (the latter both closed in 1986), under the cumbersome title of The Royal Group of Hospitals Unit of Management.

One of the most bitter debates was over the question of whether or not the Royal should still have a separate head of nursing. In the event this post was abolished and responsibility for nursing in all the hospitals was grouped together, under a new Director of Nursing Services. She was to have a number of assistant directors, each of whom would be in charge of a particular area of the Unit. As the nursing service within each of these was to function independently – rather like a series of small specialist hospitals – it meant that there was no longer a role for the Night Superintendent so this post was abolished too.

There were many who felt, rightly or wrongly, that the new system had been devised as a means to divide and conquer the nursing management of the Royal – a retribution for failure to do what they were told – and the senior nursing staff viewed the future with considerable misgiving. Morale was very low as, for the second time, some of its longest serving members had to reapply for their own jobs, or for equivalents in other parts of the hospital.

Miss Elizabeth Duffin, the Divisional Nursing Officer in the Royal Maternity Hospital, and something of a stranger to the RVH, was appointed as the first Director of Nursing Services for the Royal Group.

Miss Barratt, now, astonishingly, without a post in the hospital, left to further her career in Saudi Arabia.[3]

11   No Matron 1984 – 1988

In 1984, over a century and a half after Ann Marshall was appointed its first head nurse, the Royal lost its head of nursing. There was no longer a matron-figure whose uniformed presence alone exercised a subtle control, not only over the nurses, but over the hospital generally. No nurse, student, patient or visitor now says 'Yes Matron'. It is perhaps too early to assess the full impact of the change, but there is some evidence to show that the departure of the Matron is regretted, and not only in the Royal. There are those who would like the title as well as the office restored.[1]

For the senior nursing staff the new 'matronless' era began inauspiciously as, morale already low, they once again found a proven and familiar structure crumbling beneath them. Although the senior nursing officers had taken it in turn to deputise for Miss Barratt in her absence, the Area Health Board asked Miss H.C.C.Kerr to supervise the introduction of the new regime, possibly because, as the most recently-appointed SNO, she was less personally affected by the change than her senior colleagues.

Under the new arrangement, the Royal Group was divided into ten nursing areas with an assistant director of nursing services in charge of each and an eleventh assistant director appointed as Executive Assistant to the Director of Nursing Services. One assistant director was appointed to the RBHSC for paediatrics, and one to the RMH for obstetrics and gynaecology. The remaining eight were deployed within the Royal itself. For most, their new posts were an extension of the work they had previously been doing. Only two took on new roles. Mrs Menary, the former Night Superintendent, was put in charge of Block A, (Mrs

Simpson *née* McCullough having resigned) and Miss Betty, who had been in charge of Central Nursing Administration for some years, was moved to Geriatrics.[2] Although it was a totally new field of work for her, she set about it with characteristic conscientiousness and in the four years remaining before her retirement did much to improve the lot of this often rather neglected area.

Each assistant director now has full responsibility for providing both day and night nursing in her own area, within the limits of an allocated nursing budget. (Previously only Matron (PNO or DNO) had to deal with finance.) Each is, in effect, the matron figure in what is virtually a small hospital, but without the overall authority of a matron. Although there is, inevitably, much informal cooperation between the areas, the only formal link is at the monthly meeting between the Director of Nursing Services and her assistants.

Since this reorganisation, there have been a number of changes in the senior nursing staff. Miss H.C.C. Kerr is now DNS at the Ulster Hospital Dundonald. Miss Grant, now DNS in Belvoir Park and Forster Green Hospitals, was succeeded as ADNS (Theatres) by Miss M.P. O'Callaghan from the RBHSC. Another man, Mr Martin Bradley, took charge of the school (or college, as it is now called) when Mrs Ritchie retired in 1985. Miss F.K.Betty retired in August 1988 having spent almost all of her nursing life in the hospital, her only absences being in the pursuit of further qualifications. Sister Kate O'Hanlon retired in 1988 as Sister of the Accident and Emergency Department (Casualty), where she had given sterling service in what could be described as the hospital's 'front line', having steered her department and staff through-out twenty years of the Troubles. As the Casualty Surgeon, Mr W.M.Rutherford, once remarked, 'Running Casualty is really very simple: you have to love everybody, you have to listen to everybody; and when in doubt you just do what Sister O'Hanlon tells you!' a descrip-tion that bears more than a passing resemblance to Professor R.J.Johnstone's description of her distant predecessor Nurse Hanna.

Two of Miss Duffin's first actions, when she took office as Director of Nursing Services, were to organise a gradual reduction in the intake of student nurses – a change being pressed for by both the Area Health Board and the N.I.Board of the UKCC – and to put in train urgent preparations for the introduction of an individualised system of nurs-ing care. This system, part of the WHO medium-term programme for Nursing /Midwifery in Europe, was first recommended by the Depart-ment of Health and Social Services in the late 1970s. The recommenda-tion was later made mandatory, to be implemented before the end of 1984 – a requirement already met by a majority of hospitals in the

Miss Liz Duffin, Director of Nursing Services, Royal Group of Hospitals Unit of Management. Although the hospital no longer has a matron, Miss Duffin has overall responsibility for nursing throughout the Group.
(Miss E. Duffin, Belfast)

United Kingdom. Clinical and teaching staff co-operated in preparations for the changeover. Pilot schemes helped to iron out the more obvious initial difficulties and, in spite of some opposition from traditionalists, the system was in general use by 1986. In the same year a new training curriculum introduced the scheme to incoming student nurses.

The difference between individualized or patient-centred nursing care and the traditional or task-centred care can perhaps best be explained by looking at the traditional pattern. It had been a long-standing practice at evening bedmaking time for two nurses in a ward to devote themselves to 'doing up' very ill patients. The total needs of each patient – washing, bedmaking, treatment of mouth and pressure points, surgical dressing – were dealt with before passing on to the next. Their work, in other words, was patient-centred. In contrast, the work of the rest of nurses was task-centred. The staff nurse would first take the temperatures of all the rest of the patients, then return to do any necessary dressings. Another nurse would wash them, and return later to make their beds, change their water or clean their teeth. In earlier years, when there were only three or, very occasionally, four nurses on a ward of twenty-five or more patients, it was probably the best way to give essential care. Now, with more nurses available, it was hoped to provide a more personal service.

The Nursing Process, an American development, was chosen as the means of organising patient centred care. The Process consists of assessing the patient's needs, then devising an individually tailored plan of nursing. The effectiveness of this plan is evaluated regularly and alterations made where necessary. Like patient centred care, the Nursing Process has its antecedents in traditional practice. For example, when a patient was admitted in coma, the ward sister would be aware that preventive care was essential if the patient was not to develop bedsores or a sore mouth, and would order appropriate treatment to be started. She, or the nurses carrying out the treatment, would see if it working, and, if not, change it. Some cynics would suggest that the major difference between this and the Nursing Process was apparently the massive amount of additional paper work required in the latter.

The new system, if it really *is* new, (the ghost of Florence Nightingale might beg to differ) appears to be generally popular with student nurses who enjoy the variety of work entailed in working with smaller groups of patients. It also involves trained staff more directly in bedside nursing. Some senior nurses, while agreeing with the principle of individualized patient care, are not entirely satisfied with the present version, finding its documentation both over-simplified and over-elaborate, and as a result, unnecessarily time-consuming. Even as work is being done to adapt a system designed for a nursing service which does not use the learner nurse as an integral member of the hospital staff to suit the particular needs of the RVH, there is evidence that the Nursing Process is not being fully implemented nationally as required, and that it is being abandoned in the country of its birth.[3] Questions are being asked as to whether it lives up to the promise of its theory. The gulf between education and practice in nursing has not yet been fully bridged. It is significant that in the medical profession, teachers and practitioners are one and the same. In the nursing profession they are not.

It is interesting to recollect in the context of the Nursing Process that the first nurse employed in the Belfast Fever Hospital in Factory Row in 1797 had a maximum of six patients for whom she alone was responsible, and that the care she gave was purely nursing care, as no effective treatment was then available. Some fifty years later, when Florence Nightingale was compiling her *Notes on Nursing,* she laid

The big four.
Miss M.K. Robb,
Miss H.M.C. Barratt,
Miss F.E. Elliott and
Miss M.A. McFarland
at the Florence Elliott
Lecture, June 1986.
(Miss M.K. Robb,
Dundonald)

considerable emphasis on the need for, what in modern nursing jargon would be called, the holistic approach (i.e. considering the patient as a whole person, not just his or her nursing needs), and patient-centred care. She insisted, too, that the nurse must make an intelligent assessment of the patient's needs and be flexible in choosing the best means of care. She was also a firm believer in prevention being better than cure.[4] All of these are prominent features of the 'new' nursing. Miss Nightingale's original plans for nurse training did not develop quite as she had envisaged. She had not intended, for example, that the probationer should carry the major burden of nursing in the training hospitals. She would be pleased to see her ideas coming to the fore again.

The theoretical content of training also retains much of its original medical model, but the approach to the material is now from the nurse's rather than the medical student's point of view. For example, learning about the skeleton and muscles is related to the mobility of a patient rather than to disease of bone or muscle, and the associated practical teaching is about lifting and moving patients and maintaining muscle tone when the patient is confined to bed. Psychology and sociology relevant to the work of the nurse are given prominence. There is emphasis on the promotion of health rather than a concentration on sickness, in keeping with the current thinking, which has been given considerable publicity through the WHO project *Health for All by the Year 2000*, the Northern Ireland DHSS campaign *A Change of Heart*, and the world-wide campaign against AIDS.

There have been many smaller but no less interesting changes. Restricted visiting hours have begun to give way to open visiting. Student nurses are no longer obliged to live in – although they are still advised to do so for at least six months. As a result, and because there has been some easing of the Troubles in the vicinity of the hospital, the number of nurses living out has increased. With the resident staff now accommodated in the Towers or Bostock House, much of Musson House has become redundant. Hospital fashions have changed too. The evolution in the uniform continues. Early in 1988 it was decided to abandon the distinctive dark blue uniform for junior sisters, all sisters now wearing red. In August the last white aprons were discarded (or most of them, there are still a few who refuse to conform!) – a plastic substitute being used when necessary. Starched white collars and belts are being replaced by soft attached collars and blue belts. So far it has been possible to retain the traditional scarlet and blue for Royal nurses' uniform dresses. There is no certainty, however, that the hospital will not eventually be forced to adopt the rather insipid national uniform.

Goodbye aprons! Nurses discard their traditional white cotton aprons, 1988.

Some things, unhappily, have not changed. On Armistice Day 1987 the IRA detonated a bomb at the war memorial in Enniskillen, killing, amongst others, Marie Wilson, a third year student nurse in the Royal, and the first of its nurses to die as a result of terrorist activity.[5] Her friends and colleagues in the hospital were devastated.

The impact of the Troubles has become more subtle and insidious with the passing of time. A brief period in the early years, when common danger restored some of the old camaraderie, has been followed by the growing fear that IRA activists had infiltrated the hospital staff, a fear reinforced in August 1988 by the discovery of bomb-making equipment and ammunition in the basement. While these *could* have been placed there by an outsider, because access to the hospital as a place of healing is necessarily very easy, trust has nevertheless been undermined and a climate of suspicion created.

The Government's policies on the Health Service and staff pay have created another kind of uncertainty, and must bear much of the responsibility for yet more industrial disputes. An exhausting eight-week strike in 1986 strained the service to its limits and, once again, only great efforts on the part of the professional and administrative staff enabled the hospital to carry on.

What of the future for nursing in the Royal Victoria Hospital? Inevitably there will be change. With the weight of almost two hundred years of tradition behind it, change is not always easy to accept, and for those who have worked in the hospital over the past decade or so, the suggestion that it will almost certainly be even more rapid than in the past is almost unimaginable. The White Paper on the Health Service published early in 1989 confirms that the Government intends a radical reorganisation. In the meantime, while Parliament debates the details, a pilot scheme to be launched in the Royal in April will test a new triumveral method of controlling expenditure and increasing efficiency within the hospital. A medical clinician, an administrator and a nurse will form a team at the head of areas within the hospital – areas not dissimilar to those now supervised by the assistant directors of nursing. And that is not all! The last round of pay rises for nurses which awarded substantial increases to clinical grades, created a dilemma by excluding the assistant directors who now find themselves some £2000 a year poorer than their subordinate nursing officers, and little better off than most ward sisters! Not a happy situation. Finally the Government's acceptance of the recommendations of the UKCC's *Project 2000* includes giving the long sought for full student status to nurses in training.[6] Although the student nurse in 1988 spends a much smaller proportion of her time working in the wards than her predecessors did, nevertheless, for a service that has been built up for over a century on a foundation of learner nurse labour, this will be a traumatic change. The plan at present appears to be that in a new split training system (an eighteen month foundation period followed by a specialised second half) the new-style student nurses will spend no more than 20 per cent of their time working as part of the clinical staff. The withdrawal of student nurse labour will necessitate a consider-

A city within a city.
An aerial view of the
Royal in the 1980s.
The original wards
are to the centre right
of the picture.
(RVH, Belfast)

able increase in both untrained auxiliary staff and trained nurses, if the present level of service is to be maintained. Finding the extra staff may be a problem, particularly as it has been policy to reduce the number of nurses in training, and because of the anticipated drop in the number of school leavers.

These changes and problems lie in the immediate future. What about 1997 when Royal nursing will celebrate its bicentenary? As Florence Nightingale's remarks remind us, there is really is very little that is totally new in nursing. Fashions come and go and change at times appears to have been a substitute for progress. There will almost certainly be much wider use of computers and other sophisticated technology. Will the American robot (already in use in some of its hospitals) have arrived by then to solve the problem of staff shortages? Who knows? We will have to wait and see.

Notes

CHAPTER ONE

1. The records rarely specify which fever was responsible for an epidemic. Some later sources make educated guesses.
2. The Fever Hospital, now known as Gardner Robb House, is still in use today as part of the Belfast City Hospital complex. It was *not* part of the workhouse, merely in the same grounds and run by the same authority. The workhouse itself, with its integral infirmary, which eventually became the Belfast Union Infirmary and then the Belfast City Hospital, has been demolished and replaced by a new tower block.
3. The number varies according to different sources. Some may include the cholera beds, others not.
4. Belfast Fever Hospital, Minutes, 18 August 1834.
5. Humane, as opposed to purely custodial, treatment of the insane was first introduced about 1790 by Pinel in Paris and Tuke in York.
6. The titles of housekeeper and matron were interchangeable in the hospital until the early twentieth century. To avoid confusion the word housekeeper is used until the appointment of the first of the modern nurse/matrons (Miss Bostock) in 1901.
7. Duties of the Resident House Surgeon in 1864 included:

   No. 25. He shall have power with the concurrence of the Orderly, or one of the Medical Staff, of fining or dismissing any of the Nurses or Servants for neglect or impropriety of conduct; but he shall report the whole of the circumstances of every such case to the Board of Management at its next meeting.
   Following the establishment of the medical school in the Belfast Academical Institution in the 1830s medical students (often called pupils or 'pups') were allowed to live in the hospital for periods to obtain experience.

8. From this time the title of nurse, rather than head nurse, was normally used for the nurse in charge of a ward – the equivalent of the modern

ward sister.

9. In common with the minutes and annual reports of many other hospitals, those of the Royal Victoria and its predecessors give little space to nurses or nursing. The activities to do with fund-raising tend to dominate the records.

10. Belfast General Hospital, Annual Report, 1860.

11. Belfast Fever Hospital, Minutes, 3 April 1841.

12. Belfast Fever Hospital, Minutes, 27 April 1828; Belfast General Hospital, Minutes, Vol 1863-67.

13. Belfast General Hospital, Minutes, 19 March 1836.

14. The local name for the Lancastrian School in Frederick Street.

15. Johnstone, R.J. 'Frederick Street, Personal Reminiscences.' *Ulst. Med. J.* Vol.9, No1, April 1940, pp3-5.

CHAPTER TWO

1. 1865: Founding of Belfast Skin Hospital
   1867: Belfast Ophthalmic Hospital
   1871: Benn Eye, Ear and Throat Hospital
   1872: Ulster Hospital for Women and Children
   1873: Belfast Hospital for Sick Children; Samaritan Hospital
   1875: Throne Children's Hospital
   1876: Rescue Home (Maternity)
   1883: Mater Infirmorum Hospital
   1886: Throne Sanitorium
   1890: Forster Green Hospital
   1893: Nervous Diseases Hospital

2. The only previous organised training scheme for nurses in Ulster had been one introduced in the Belfast Union Infirmary in the 1850s for training pauper inmates. While apparently well–organised, this scheme appears to have been short-lived, probably because of the decreasing numbers of able-bodied paupers available.

3. Adam Macrory's church work was commemorated in the naming of the Macrory Memorial Presbyterian Church in Duncairn Gardens, Belfast.

4. The Visiting Medical Staff, which met separately, appointed two representatives to the Board. In later years, when the Visiting Medical Staff became too large, its business was conducted by the Medical Staff Committee.

5. Not all training schools based on the Nightingale pattern were separated from the hospital as in Belfast and Liverpool. The Matron of St Thomas's, for example, was responsible for both school and hospital.

6. Miss Nightingale appears to have been rather ambivalent about private nursing. She believed that the first duty of Nightingale-trained nurses was to go out and train others and therefore that private nursing was a waste of both time and talent. At the same time she appreciated the difficulties under which they worked, in the absence of a doctor and

without the support of the facilities of a hospital.

7. The Nightingale Fund, contributed by the public as a tribute to Florence Nightingale's work in the Crimea was used to establish nurse training schools in a few selected hospitals. As financial backer the Fund (and through it Miss Nightingale herself) had a considerable say in the running of these schools. Only nurses trained in schools under the auspices of the Fund were properly entitled to call themselves Nightingale nurses.

8. Belfast Nurses Home and Training School, Minutes, 6 September 1892.

9. Belfast General Hospital, Minutes, 9 May 1874. Members of the Board took it in turn to act as Orderly, in which capacity they made inspections of the hospital on behalf of the Board.

10. Belfast Nurses Home, Minutes, June 1874.

11. *Belfast Newsletter*, 12, 13 December 1875.

12. Belfast Royal Hospital, Minutes, 18 December 1875.

13. Letter, Florence Nightingale to Henry Bonham Carter, 25 January 1876, British Museum, Add. Mss. 47719.

14. Belfast Royal Hospital, Medical Staff Report Book, 20 December, 1894.

15. The only source for the original minutes of the Nurses Home is in notes made from them by the late Colonel J.V. Forrest, former Medical Superintendent of the RVH, in preparation for his book *A Short Note on the Origins and Early History of Modern Nursing in Northern Ireland*. His notes are now in the medical library of The Queen's University of Belfast.

16. When the Royal National Pension Fund for Nurses was inaugurated in 1898, most Irish nurses were ineligible because of the lower rates of pay in Ireland.

17. Personal communication from Miss May Flack, daughter of Marianne Harden, probationer in the Belfast Royal Hospital in the 1890s.

CHAPTER THREE

1. More uses were found for the Plenum system than could possibly have been envisaged by the installers. Medical students found it to be an excellent vehicle for practical jokes. By walking up the main ventilation tunnel and then crawling down one of its offshoots it was possible to call up the ventilators to the night nurses who, thinking it was a patient, searched in vain for the caller. An even more bizarre use was found for the tunnel after the first air raid on Belfast in 1941 when Crowe, the hospital plumber, brought his family into it for safety, remaining undetected there for some time.

2. All nurses in training were probationers. According to their place in the ward pecking order, which was strictly according to length of service, they were classified as juniors, extras (rarely, and only if there was surplus staff on the ward) or as seniors.

3. Members of the Visiting Medical Staff were generally referred to as consultants.

4. Sir Frank Montgomery.

5. Until the late 1940s, the nursing staff in Extern at night was responsible for laying out bodies, often accident victims, brought to the hospital for confirmation of death.

6. Some nurses enlisted for specific periods, other for 'the duration'.

7. Other hospitals were even worse off. Down County Infirmary had a probationer acting as Matron for three weeks! Personal communication, Miss A. Campbell.

8. The age of entry was reduced to twenty-one in 1918 when the wider choice of available employment was affecting recruitment.

9. Belfast District Lunatic Asylum 82nd Annual Report, 1911; C.J. Maggs, *The Origins of General Nursing* (1983) p.90.

10. The nurse (my mother Mary (Molly) Best) later spent four years as an Army nurse in places as diverse as France, Egypt, the Mediterranean and Aberdeen.

CHAPTER FOUR

1. Northern Ireland did not have a Ministry of Health until 1944.

2. Nurses washed everything used by the patients except ordinary laundry and dishes. Soiled bed-linen, however, had to be sluiced clean of blood or excrement before being sent to the Laundry, and the dishes had to be washed on the wardsmaid's evening off.

3. The Asylum had been used as a war hospital after its psychiatric patients had been transferred to Purdysburn.

4. Pensions had been given to Poor Law Union workhouse nurses since the nineteenth century.

5. The coming of the fork-lift truck brought a dramatic reduction in the number suffering from this complaint. Personal communication, Sir Ian Fraser.

6. At first this break was for lunch (tea, bread and butter) – breakfast having been served at 6.30 a.m. However, after 1938 an early cup of tea was provided at 6.30 a.m. and breakfast was served at 8.30 a.m. and 9 a.m.

7. Miss Musson was a talented artist in both oils and water colour, a member of the Royal Ulster Academy of Arts, and frequently exhibited her work.

8. The Voluntary Aid Detachment – a group of women who worked as untrained assistants to service nurses during the First World War.

9. The last remains of Jeffries' shop in Cromac Street were demolished in 1986.

10. *Nurses Registration (Ireland) Act,* 1919. 9&10 Geo. 5. c.96.

11. The first tutor in the Union Infirmary was Miss Winifred Vance who was paid £200 a year (the same as Miss Musson was getting).

12. Block study was a method of organising the theoretical side of nurse training. Instead of having to attend lectures and study for exams in their off duty hours, nurses were taken from the wards to spend 'blocks' of time in the school. At first, only short periods for revision before exams were allowed. Later, these were extended and all lectures as well as

study were included in study block time.

13. Personal communication, Miss Peggy Nuttall.

14. Comments in nurses' records.

15. The College of Nursing was granted a Royal Charter in 1928.

16. Earlier, at least two nurses, Miss Dorothy Melville and Miss Daly the Sister Tutor, had been given instruction by Mr Leeman leading to a professional qualification in radiography.

17. It was 1949 before a school of physiotherapy was finally established in the hospital. The close link between nursing and the Massage Department had been broken in 1943 when Matron, at the request of the Visiting Medical Staff, ceased to be involved in the appointment of masseuses.

18. The increase was funded from the savings made by increasing the training contract to four years. The main purpose of these awards was to economise in the staffing of the Maternity Hospital, pupil midwives performing the same role there as the probationer did in other hospitals. The cost of the scholarship – the pupil's training fee – was appreciably less than the cost of employing a fully qualified midwife.

CHAPTER FIVE

1. Fisk, Robert *In Time of War* 1985, p.494

2. This was a new sub-committee of the Board's Nursing Committee.

3. A second committee, the Taylor Committee, was set up to deal with nursing in Scotland and its recommendations, rather than those of the original Rushcliffe Committee, were adopted for Northern Ireland.

CHAPTER SIX

1. For a time this had to be administered by the Houseman three-hourly night and day – with the injection site prepared by the application of an icebag for twenty minutes beforehand. Broken sleep proved exhausting for the doctors, so permission was given for the Junior Night Sister to deputize for the night-time doses.

2. The new building was named Quin House after the Chairman of the Board of Management, Senator Herbert Quin.

3. The 'septic' theatre was used exclusively for minor surgery in infected tissue – boils, abscesses etc.

4. Originally a children's hospital attached to the Royal, and previously used only for convalescents.

5. A few hospitals opted to remain independent. Sanitoria were already under the central control of the Northern Ireland Tuberculosis Authority, established in 1946.

6. Many members of the Board later served on the Hospital Management Committee.

7. *Social Services Agreement Act (N.I.),*1949. 13 & 14 Geo.6. c.3.

8. The Royal was one of very few hospitals, if not the only one, whose

nurses wore white shoes and stockings, a fact commented upon (favourably) when they attended outside functions in uniform.

9. It was at Sister Brown's insistence that Miss Elliott returned to Northern Ireland. When the Whiteabbey post fell vacant in 1943, the hospital was going through a particularly difficult period, so Sister Brown wrote to her in Edinburgh to say it was her *duty* (or the duty of someone like her from Northern Ireland) to return and do something about remedying the situation. Obedient to her conscience, and Sister Brown, she came.

10. Health Service pensions were not given to nurses who had reached sixty-five before July 1948. They were, however, provided for out of hospital 'free funds' – money retained by the hospital when it was taken over by the Hospitals Authority.

11. Newly appointed ward orderlies were given a short course of instruction in the school to help them understand and fit into hospital routine.

12. The first of these girls, Iba Etuk, now Mrs Amobi, has since gone on to become a distinguished figure in Nigeria, where she became head of a university school of nursing, and in international nursing circles.

13. At least one short course of lectures on flower arranging was given by a floral artist who, as a patient, had been appalled by the way expensive and beautiful flowers were hastily stuffed into totally unsuitable vases by busy nurses.

14. Shortly before this, it had been made compulsory for all nurses appointed to senior posts in mental hospitals to have dual qualification in general and mental nursing.

15. Miss Creighton later returned to the main school and in turn was succeeded by Miss Elias Dodds and then Mrs Elizabeth Fullerton.

16. She received the Baird cup, presented by Sir William Baird.

17. The College had been given a grant by the Nuffield Provincial Hospitals Trust to enable it to rent accommodation and establish nurse education courses in Northern Ireland. The grant was due to end in 1952. Substantial capital was needed if it was to be able to continue its work.

CHAPTER SEVEN

1. In 1959 the first completely new general hospital to be built in the British Isles after the Second World War, was opened at Altnagelvin in Londonderry, followed by the first units of the new Ulster Hospital at Dundonald in 1962. The new Erne Hospital was opened in Enniskillen in 1964. In 1959 the first artificial kidney was purchased for the Belfast City Hospital, and a cobalt unit for the N.I. Radiotherapy Centre.

2. The former was used instead for convalescent and long stay patients, and the latter as a drug abuse centre.

3. She was also responsible for the work of the dental surgery assistants. In 1978 a two-year training for them was started in association with the school of nursing. Prior to this only trained DAs were employed.

4. Unlike other nurses' homes this was not funded by the hospital or

Hospitals Authority but by a limited liability company formed for the purpose. The Tower has 96 double and single flats for junior medical staff and nurses. Preference was given to trained nurses but, when flats were available, third year nurses were accepted. The rent in 1966 for a single furnished flat was £13 a month, and for a double flat £16, including heating, rates and portering service. By 1988 these had risen to £85.75 and £108.263.

5. Known technically as Belfast sinks.

6. This grade was known in other hospitals as a nursing assistant, but Miss Elliott refused to have the title 'nursing' used for any personnel except those authorized by the *Nurses Act (N.I.)*, 1946, which had made it illegal for any person to work as a nurse other than state registered or enrolled nurses or those in training for these qualifications.

7. There appear to have been no hard feelings afterwards however, as both Miss Elliott and Brigadier Davidson (the GMS) later served amicably together on a new group nursing advisory committee with the Matrons and Senior Tutors of all three hospitals, and the Group Secretary and Administrative Officer.

8. To the great relief of the student nurses Miss Mitchell provided stencilled lecture notes – the improvement Miss Musson had unsuccessfully tried to have funded some years before.

9. The other hospitals involved were the Toronto Western and Massachusetts General, Boston. Tutors taking part in the scheme spent an academic year in one hospital and two months in the other. The long term tutors visiting the Royal were Miss Adele Sowa from Toronto and Miss Constance Holleran from Boston. Miss Holleran has since become Executive Secretary to the International Council of Nurses.

10. The Exchange Report was written by Professor Joan Woodward, Sociologist, London University.

11. The design was submitted by a student nurse who had previously worked in the Erne Hospital.

CHAPTER EIGHT

1. Miss Galbraith, was Royal-trained and formerly Sister in Wards 15 and 16. She later became a member of the commissioning team for the Belfast City Hospital Tower Block.

2. Extern was occupied for a time by the Army and then shared between Cardiology and the Catering Department, which based its plated meals service for the main wards there.

3. The surgeons and anaethetists wrote of their experiences in a series of articles in the *British Medical Journal*, which were later published under the title *Surgery of Violence* and generously dedicated to the nursing staff.

4. Although the rule against nurses in training marrying was generally observed, like all rules it could be bent. One engaged student nurse in

the late 1950s, whose fiancé was about to return to North America, was given permission by Matron (Miss F.E. Elliott) to marry before he left, returning after her honeymoon to live in the nurses' home and complete her training.

5. Min.of H., S.H.H.D. *Rep.of the Ctte. on Senior Nursing Staff* (Salmon Report) (1966)

6. Min.H.S.S.(N.I.) *The Administrative Structure of the Health and Personal Social Services in N.I.* (1969); Min.H.S.S.(N.I.) *Consultative Document on the Restructuring of the Health and Personal Social Services in N.I.* (1971)

CHAPTER NINE

1. Some years earlier two other new areas of nursing had been developed. In 1960 a full-time staff nurse was allocated to the Radio-isotope Department, and in 1965 a control of infection sister was appointed; the latter was later given responsibility for this work in all the hospitals in the Group.

CHAPTER TEN

1. Prior to this there had been an number of variations in the curricula of the different countries, particularly in enrolled nurse training.

2. Interestingly enough, research on these often disputed ratios shows that it was not the number of nurses, but the quality of their teaching that was the deciding factor.

3. Her links with her former colleagues remain strong, particularly through the medium of the Florence Elliott Lecture Committee. The lecture, in honour of the former Matron of the hospital, was Miss Barratt's own brainchild.

CHAPTER ELEVEN

1. Findings of a national survey conducted by the *Nursing Times*. *Nursing Times* Jy.20-26,1988

2. The Geriatric Department included Haypark Hospital (until it closed in 1986) and the Throne Hospital.

3. *Nursing Standard* July 16,1988 p.15

4. Nightingale, F. *Notes on Nursing* G. Duckworth & Co.Ltd, 1861, rev.ed.

5. Since 1968 three other members of staff have been killed as a result of terrorist activity: Janet Bereen, physiotherapist and daughter of consultant anaesthetist Dr J.F.Bereen, died in the bombing of the Abercorn restaurant; Gerald Tucker, mortuary porter, was shot coming off duty; Robin Shields, ambulance controller, was shot at his desk in the Ambulance Depot.

6. A plan prepared by the UKCC for nurse education in the 1990s and onwards.

Appendix A

Belfast Fever Hospital Regulations and Duties for Nurses: 1832

It is requisite that each Nurse, as well as each Assistant, must be able to read and write.

No person can fill the office of Nurse, without having served as Assistant.

Every Nurse is entitled to leave of absence two evenings in each week – Sunday and also on Tuesday or Thursday Evening, and must return at a Quarter past Nine o'clock in Winter, from 1st October till 31st March, and a Quarter till Ten in Summer, from lst April till 30th September.

Any nurse or other Servant trespassing the above Regulations, will, for the first offence be fined – for the second, dismissed.

No Nurse will be allowed out of the Hospital any day till after the visit of the Physician or Surgeon in attendance.

Every Nurse is expected to rise at Seven o'clock in the morning;

The duty of each will be:

To receive from the Night Nurse a correct history of the Patient during the night, marking well any change or other important circumstance which may have occurred to any patient during the night.

To see as accurately as possible that Wine, Nourishment, and Medicine, have been delivered to each patient as was ordered.

To have the face and hands of each Patient washed thoroughly every morning, and to give notice to the Porter when any may require to be shaved.

To superintend and assist in the regulation of the Wards, and also in the distribution of food.

To have the Prescription and Case Books as well as pens and ink in their proper place and be dressed, ready to attend the Physician or Surgeon in his visit to the Wards. As soon as the visit is over, she shall at once proceed to carry out the instructions of the Medical Attendant, and give every assistance to the Clinical Clerks, and Dresser of the Wards.

During the remainder of the day she will be as much as possible in the Wards, administering the Medicines, Nourishment, &c. which may have been ordered.

When the Night Nurse comes on duty, at Ten o'clock, she will take her round the Wards, and point out to her each particular case, and give those directions and instructions which may tend to the comfort and welfare of the patients during the night.

Each Nurse shall be held accountable for the negligence or want of attention in any of her Assistants; also, for the state of the Wards over which she has charge.

Each Assistant Nurse is expected to rise every morning at Six o'clock.

Her duties are – to obey the directions of the Nurses under whom she is placed.

To wash and thoroughly cleanse each Ward and Lobby daily, as well as the stairs leading from those Lobbies.

To empty all slops or other nuisances, and to properly wash the vessels containing such.

She will carry up the food and give it to the Patients, always under the guidance of the Nurse; after meals she shall immediately have all such vessels washed and put in their proper place, as were required for such food.

The Night Nurse is expected to come on duty at Ten o'clock, at which time she will at once proceed to receive from the Day Nurse the directions and instructions which each Patient may require. To see that she has received proper supplies of Nourishment, Drinks, and Medicines, during the night – and to give immediate notice to the Resident Medical Officer, of any bad symptom or change which may occur to any Patient. In the morning she will relate to the Day Nurse anything of importance which may have occurred in the Wards during the night. She will make up the beds and place them in a settled state.

N.B. – The infringement of any of the above Rules, will, for the first two offences, be visited with a fine – for the third, dismissal.

No Nurse or Assistant is allowed, on any account, to punish any patient of this Hospital, for disobedience or misbehaviour in the Wards, by stopping their supplies of food or otherwise. She is expected to treat them all with kindness and tenderness; and if any Patient should happen to become ungovernable, she will at once report the circumstance.

DUTIES OF HEAD NURSE

1. To receive all Patients admitted into the Hospital; to see that they are thoroughly washed and clean, and supplied with clean linen and bedding, and their clothes immediately ticketed and stored.

2. To see that the beds are made, and the Wards well cleaned out and aired, every morning.

3. To see that the Patients are kept clean at all times.

4. To see that they are suppplied with their possets, and that they are properly and comfortably supplied with their rations.

5. To have the sole charge of all the clothing and furniture in the Hospital, bed and bedding, and to make up and mend when required.

6. To have charge of the Wash-house, the washing of the clothes, and the forwarding to and receiving from the Wash-house of all clothes;

7. To have charge of all the nurses, night and day medicine nurses and assistants, and look after all articles of clothing &c. entrusted to them.

8. To know when the nurses go out and return, and to look strictly after their conduct, and report to the House-Surgeon any impropriety or misconduct.

9. To visit all the Wards, on all opportunities; to look particularly after the state of the beds, bedding, and the wards generally, and to see that both day and night nurses are always at their posts.

Appendix B

Green View,
Dunmurry
Co.Antrim

Tuesday 19th, 12/71

Madam,

My excuse for troubling you with a letter is this. We are abt. to establish a "Nurses' Home and Training School" in Belfast in connexion with the Genl. Hospital to supply a want wh. is sorely felt in the *Hospital* private families indeed by all classes rich and poor.

At our first Meeting of the "Board of Management" held yesterday the Committee passed a resolution "that the Hon. Secretary put herself in communication with Miss Nightingale to request her most kindly to give us her valuable aid and advice in procuring a Lady Superintendent for the Home " May I earnestly hope that you will kindly do so. We want a really first class Lady Superintendent, a Xian lady. It is not necessary for me to tell y*ou* what we require. May I also request (I do so feeling I am asking almost too much knowing the demands upon yr time) that you will read the accompanying report and if you wd. make any remarks upon it it wd. be a great boon. We are very anxious to commence our Home work as soon as possible. Of course nothing can be done till we get our Lady Superintendent.

> Trusting you will not consider this an intrusion I remain
> Madam with much respect
> Yrs most obt.
> (signed) Minnie Otway,
> Hon. Secretary

Letter Minnie Otway to Florence Nightingale 19 December 1871
Greater London Record Office, Bonham Carter Papers,
HI/SST/NC2/VI 71

Appendix C

Constitution of Belfast Nurses Home and Training School
annotated by Florence Nightingale

(Miss Nightingale's initialled comments are jotted in the margins of the
Constitution alongside the relevant passages which she had heavily underlined.)

Constitution: The internal duties of the Home are to be under the immediate
supervison of the ladies, who form portion of the Board of Management.
FN: NO – under the Supt.

Constitution: Probationers to be at least under training two months in a
surgical ward, then two months in a medical ward then four months in a
surgical, and again four months in a medical ward; thus completing twelve
months.
FN: This should be left to the Supt.

Constitution: A limited number of lady pupils should they offer will be received
into the Home, and trained for nursing in private families.
FN: "Lady Pupils" will never take *"private"* nursing and ought not, if they
would.

Constitution: To the Ladies Committee will pertain, in addition to the general
supervision of the Home, the duty of inspecting all applicants, of inquiry into
their eligibility, and of recommending women from twenty-five to thirty-five
years of age, able to read and write, as probationer nurse for a period of at
least twelve months;
FN: Not to the "Ladies Committee" – to the Supt.

Constitution: …the Ladies' Committee are to assist the Superintendent in
allocating their [nurses] duties…
FN: "Duties" must be left to the Lady Superintendent.

Constitution: …a distinct building, convenient to the hospital…capable of
containing a staff of nurses…sufficient for hospital and private nursing…
FN: Hospital Nurses must live in the Hospital.

Constitution: The Ladies' Committee shall make such Rules as they may
consider necessary for the internal management…
FN: "Internal management" must be left to the Lady Supt.

Constitution: Queries for nurses
4. Are you willing to attend on the poor as well as the rich?
FN: This can never be – is making the nursing of the *poor* subsidiary – which
in every Institution combining private nursing with public, there is always too
much danger of its becoming. This is a constant difficulty. But here it is
almost obtruded that the nursing of the poor is to be subsidiary.

Greater London Record Office. Bonham Carter Papers. Hl/ST/NC2/VI 71

Appendix D

London, January 29, 1874

My Dear Madam,

I have so very deep an interest in your Belfast Nurses' Home and Training School that, unwilling as I should feel at any time, and at this time doubly so, bowed down as I am with sorrow and illness and overwork, I cannot, but as you desire it, do as you wish, and put down a few words in answer to your questions, although, really, all that I have to say are truisms, just as much as, 'put your hats on your heads and shoes on your feet'. A good nurse must be a good woman; a sick woman cannot be a healthy nurse. To induce a good and respectable young woman to your institution, to induce them to stay, to keep them in health, and above deterioration either of mind, soul, or body, you must give them respectable and healthy accommodation, good food, and the moral and physical helps necessary to keep women up in hospital life, which, after all is said and done that man can say and do for the best, remains, and always will remain, a great drain upon woman's life, bodily and moral; Otherwise, women will 'keep themselves up', as within the remembrance of us all they have kept themselves up, by drink, by pilfering among the patients, and by the excitement of immoral behaviour. To draw a class into the nursing career who are above these things, and to keep them above the very temptation to these things, must be the very first object of all who wish to improve hospitals and nursing generally.

For no doubt can exist either that women in hospital life require more helps to keep them straight than in family life or domestic service, or they receive fewer. From my own experience of nurses' training schools in reformed hospitals, I should say that quite as many candidates present themselves from the highest motives out of the uneducated as out of the educated classes.

To come for the sake of earning a livelihood is not only compatible with, but may be one of the highest motives. For to support destitute relations to be honourably independent, is a high motive in itself.

But the highest motives wear off and nursing life becomes only a hardening routine, if we give no food, or not proper food to the best qualities of these women; and this of course happens more quickly among the uneducated than the educated, and more surely in Hospital life than in any other.

I appeal to all who have any experience whether this is not a truism, and I appeal to all who used to say 'We did very well before', whether they have not now begun to say – they need not say it out loud – 'We did very badly before'.

One of the first essentials for nurses, and for night nurses if possible even more than for day, is that each should have a sleeping compartment or room, with window and partition up to the ceiling, each to herself; and, as it is most inconvenient and expensive (if not impossible) to contrive these out of an ordinary dwelling-house, it is found to be necessary (and cheaper in the end) to build at once something after the construction of the Liverpool Nurses' Home (Miss Merryweather) or after that of the 'Nightingale Home', St Thomas's Hospital, London; where, I may say by the way the less ornament there is, the better would it look. To have the best drainage and sanitary arrangements in these Nurses' Homes is of course of first-rate importance, and, if not well provided for at first, can never be provided afterwards, except at inordinate expense. There must be thorough means of giving fresh air to every corner of the 'Home', good warming arrangement, convenient bath-room and sink, w.c. accommodation on each floor, a roomy dining-room, and good kitchen arrangements, unless they alraeady exist in the hospital, if possible, a classroom; as this building is meant for a Training School and may ultimately supply all Ulster with nurses, a sick room, and hot and cold water laid on on each floor.

These things are either absolutely necessary to preserve the nurse's health, or they save, if properly provided, such an amount of labour as only persons of experience can estimate.

Shall it be said that thriving, prosperous Belfast, justly celebrated for progress in Ireland, justly celebrated for its medical schools and science, shall be behind Liverpool and London in securing the essentials of a good nursing school?

Would you wish a woman to come to you who does not care for decent privacy? Would your committee wish a woman to nurse their own wives or sons or daughters who had no care for this? Could she be a good nurse? Yet private nursing is an acknowledged part of your institution.

Or do you expect a woman to stay, to remain a good woman, or become a better woman, if she wishes for decent privacy, and has it not?

It is impossible for a woman in the unavoidable drive of the hospital life, if she has no corner where she can be alone and read a verse to herself for one little moment, morning and night, not to become quite other than you would wish to have about the sick and the dying.

These are no high-flown theories; they are my actual experience with the poor, hard-working, moral women; – and do you wish to have those who are not? – by no means distinguished either in education or anything else from their fellows, who say to me that they 'can't sleep unless they have a place to themselves, however small, to sit down in and read, if it be only a line or two, before getting into bed. If I can do that I sleep like a top'

And surely, were it merely a matter of health, we ought to give them that.

Then, most reformed hospitals wish to attract the gentler sort of women, gentlewomen, in fact, as an important leaven among the nurses in a training school; and I am far from saying that the advantage is all on the side of the nurses, though nurse-probationers have said, 'We don't do when we have ladies among us what they think coarse.'

This is certainly not the highest motive. But the forming of any good habit is good, and this, too, is a truism.

The decent habits formed in a decent home in childhood and girlhood are walls of good conduct, which many a woman tempted to evil in after life finds it impossible to overstep, and so is saved.

And what are we, if we do not do what we can to build up these walls of good habits to keep women from sin.

And no one will say – although you cannot expect gentlewomen to come and be trained, if you do not give them a proper 'Home' – that they need it more, or so much as the uneducated; quite the reverse.

The uneducated, the common run of hospital nurses, need it more than the gentlewoman, to keep them from falling into the drinking, light-characered, light-fingered, altogether untrustworthy, untrained, floating population of hospital Nurses of twenty years ago, women who took hospital service because they could get no other. And does anyone really suppose that such women as these will carry our medical orders, if at all, as well as the trained respectable, sober, solid woman?

To sum up – a good nurse must be a good woman, and also a healthy woman; and, as a general rule, you cannot have a good woman unless you place her in the circumstances (among which good accommodaiton, good food, good companionship, good supervision, are of primary importance) which keep a woman good, and keep her healthy; ; for hospital life is at the best a great drag on body and mind; and I object to apologise, and do for these truisms.

Lastly – as to patching, repairing, adding to, and re-laying out old buildings, I know but one experience on this subject, and it is also my own.

Don't throw good money after bad, build new; if you build, build wisely; of course you have a new building to suit its purpose, at moderate outlay. If you add and repair an old building not even originally constructed to suit their purpose, and certain to be deficient in the most essential requisites of health and comfort – you have at the end of all your additions and re-constructions a bad building, at immoderate outlay. Finally, I wish the Belfast Nursing Institution 'God speed' with all my heart and soul; and I would like to see it outstrip all its contemporaries that they may in their own turn outstrip the Belfast; and so healthy race be kept up for a thousand years and a day, to the great good of all sick people, and all active women all over the world. – And pray believe me, my dear madam, ever your faithful servant,

(Signed) Florence Nightingale

Letter to Miss Otway, Hon. Secretary of the Belfast Nurses Home and Training School from Florence Nightingale, January 29, 1874.
Forrest, J.V. Abstracts from Minutes of Belfast Nurses Home and Training School, 1871-1935.

Appendix E

Nurses' Home and Training School
Frederick Street,

30th October 1875

Dear Sir,

A very serious complication has arisen again between the Home and the Hospital Board when neither Miss Bourne our Lady Superintendent or anyone connected with 'The Home' had any idea but that everything was working in the most perfect harmony and in the best order. On first hearing of it I asked one of the Staff and he said 'I never heard anyone express the very slightest wish to have the nursing arrangement changed or any dissatisfaction with the present state of affairs'. The complication is this. The Doctors wish to get the power of dismissal etc. over the nurses again into their own hands. This is the third time and they have *to-day* passed a rule at the hospital to this effect – without even consulting the Committee of the Home whose nurses they are. I called a Committee meeting last week and I made a statement on the enclosed [enclosure not available] when a deputation was appointed to wait to-day upon the Hospital Committee to say how serious this was to take the authority over the nurses from the Lady Superintendent and that to prevent any misunderstanding there should be a consultation between the two Boards. But the Hospital Committee determined that they would not open the question again and passed this rule.

He (the House Surgeon) shall have power with the concurrence of the Superintendent (Hospital Superintendent Captain Cos) or one of the Medical Staff of suspending any of the nurses for neglect or impropriety of conduct; but he shall report the whole of the circumstances of every such case (after) to the Lady Superintendent of the Nurses' Home, also to the Board of Management (Hospital) at its next meeting.

I must now call a meeting of our committee to see what steps we shall take. Would you kindly let me have your views upon this matter as your opinion would carry much weight with our Board as to their course and prevent their yielding.

Knowing as I do from personal knowledge the undercurrent at work I have no hesitation in saying it would be fatal to the morale of the Home and nurses, so much so if this is yielded I will resign from any connection with the Home. Had they conceded to putting in 'in the absence of the Lady Superintendent' – but they refused decidedly. So if granted the Home will be a sham.

The nurses are hired, paid, provided for by us and the management to be taken out of our hands. You will, I am certain give me your opinion so that I can make use of it. I regret much being obliged to trouble you but the broad interest both Miss Nightingale and you have taken in our work here and my great anxiety to obtain your advice is my excuse – I think there should be an appeal to the public as there is to be a return to the old system. Will you kindly send your reply to my own address 'Greenview', Dunmurry, Co. Antrim as I am anxious to get it at the earliest moment.

I write from here so as not to lose a post. Would Mrs Wardroper also give me an opinion of how this is to work,

Very faithfully yours,
(signed) M. Otway

Letter Miss Minnie Otway to Mr Henry Bonham Carter, 10 October 1875.
Greater London Record Office, Bonham Carter Papers H1/ST/NC 18/12/46

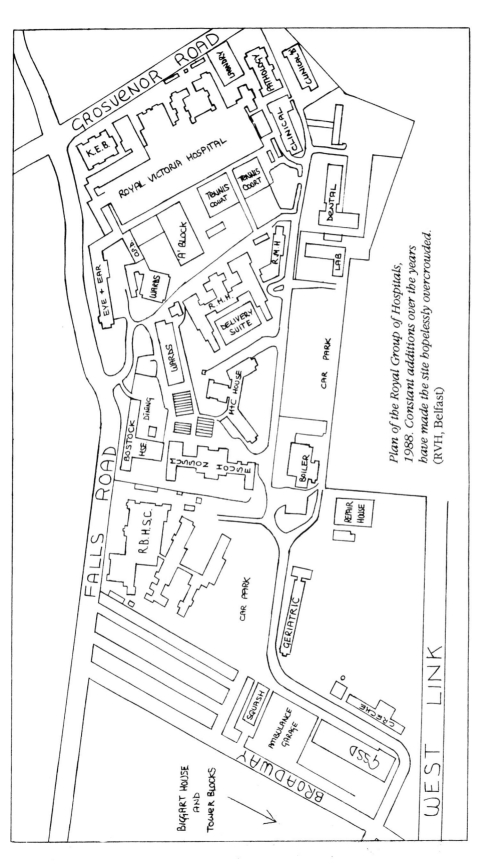

Plan of the Royal Group of Hospitals, 1988. Constant additions over the years have made the site hopelessly overcrowded. (RVH, Belfast)

Select Bibliography

Much of the background material for this book was obtained in the process of research for a thesis on the development of nursing in Northern Ireland which contains a full bibliography and in which due acknowledgement is made. The following bibliography contains only sources directly relating to the RVH and its nursing and those sources referred to in the text.

I. PRIMARY SOURCES

A. MANUSCRIPT (including typescript and oral sources)

British Library
Nightingale Papers

Eastern Health and Social Services Board
North and West Belfast District Hospital and Community Nursing Reports

Greater London Record Office
Bonham Carter Papers

The Queen's University of Belfast, Medical Library
Belfast Nurses Home and Training School; Abstract of Minutes by J.V.Forrest.

Royal College of Nursing, N.I. Board
Belfast Branch: Minutes
N.I.Committee: Minutes
N.I.Board: Minutes
Miscellaneous Records

Royal Victoria Hospital, Belfast. Archives
Belfast Fever Hospital: Minutes
Belfast Hospital: Minutes
Belfast General Hospital: Minutes
Belfast Royal Hospital: Minutes; Staff Report Books; Sub-Committees' Minutes.
Royal Victoria Hospital: Accounts; Finance Committee Minutes; Matrons' Reports; Nursing Committee Minutes; Miscellaneous papers (uncatalogued).

Royal Victoria Hospital, Belfast
Letters and oral communications from former and serving staff.

Royal Victoria Hospital, Belfast. Nursing Administration
Records of Nurses
Miscellaneous records

Royal Victoria Hospital School of Nursing/ Belfast Northern College of Nursing
Miscellaneous records
Oral communications from former and serving staff

UKCC, N.I.Board
Joint Nursing and Midwives Council: Minutes and miscellaneous records
N.I.Council for Nurses and Midwives: Miscellaneous records
Registers of Nurses N.I.

B. PRINTED

1. Legislation

Nurses Registration (Ireland) Act, 1919. 9 & 10 Geo.5 c.96
Social Services Agreement Act (N.I.), 1949. 13 & 14 Geo.6 c3
Nurses and Midwives Act (N.I.), 1959. 7 ELiz. 2 c19c
The Nurses Midwives and Health Visitors Act, 1979. ch 36

2. Reports and other Government Documents

Min. of H., S.H.H.D. *Rep. of the Ctte. on Senior Nursing Staff* (Salmon Report) (1966)

Min.H.S.S.(N.I.) *The Administrative Structure of the Health and Personal Social Services in N.I.* (1969)

Min.H.S.S.(N.I.) *Consultative Document on the Restructuring of the Health and Personal Social Services in N.I.* (1971)

II. SECONDARY SOURCES

1. Journals

Belfast Newsletter; Belfast Telegraph; British Journal of Nursing;
Nursing Mirror; Nursing Standard; Nursing Times;
RVH League of Nurses Magazine; Ulster Medical Journal

2. Books

Allison, R.S. *The Seeds of Time.* Belfast, 1972
Baly, M.E. *Florence Nightingale and the Nightingale Legacy.* 1987
Bardon, Jonathan, *Belfast, An Illustrated History* Belfast, 1982
Beckett, J.C. et al. *Belfast, The Making of the City.* Belfast, 1983
Burdett,H. *Official Nursing Directory.* 1898
Forrest, J.V. *Short Note on the Origin and Early History of Modern Nursing in Northern Ireland.* Belfast, 1936
Grey, M.E. *Progressive Professional Nursing.* Edinburgh, 1950
Maggs, C.J. *The Origins of General Nursing.* 1983
Malcolm, A.G. *History of the Belfast General Hospital.* Belfast, 1851 facs.ed.
in Calwell,H.G. *Andrew Malcolm of Belfast.* Belfast, 1976
Marshall, R. *The Royal Victoria Hospital, Belfast, 1903-1953.* Belfast, 1953
M'Gimpsey, C. intro. *Bombs on Belfast: the Blitz 1941.* Belfast, 1984
Nightingale, F. *Notes on Nursing.* 1859. (1861 ed.repr. 1952)
Seymour, Lucy *Florence Nightingale's Nurses.* 1960
Strain, R.W.M. *Belfast and its Charitable Society.* Belfast, 1961
Watson, J.K. *A Handbook of Nursing.* 1899

3. Thesis

Donaldson, Margaret   The Development of Nursing in Northern Ireland. D.Phil Thesis. N.U.U. 1983

Index